Happy 18th

Jo & Colin.

AMATEUR GUNSMITHING

AMATEUR GUNSMITHING

Desmond Mills and Mike Barnes

THE BOYDELL PRESS

© Desmond Mills and Mike Barnes 1986

First published 1986 by The Boydell Press
an imprint of Boydell & Brewer Ltd
PO Box 9, Woodbridge, Suffolk IP12 3DF
and Dover, New Hampshire, USA

British Library Cataloguing in Publication Data

Mills, Desmond
   Amateur gunsmithing.
   1. Gunsmithing—Amateurs' manuals
   I. Title   II. Barnes, Mike
   683'.4   TS535

   ISBN 0-85115-455-7

Erratum: The final sentence of the jacket blurb should read:

. . . *Sporting Gun* magazine, the country's biggest-selling shooting monthly.

Shooting Times is the country's biggest-selling shooting magazine, and
we have been asked to point this out by the management of
Burlington Publishing Co.

Library of Congress Cataloging in Publication Data applied for

Printed in Great Britain by
Camelot Press, Southampton

Contents

Acknowledgements

The authors are grateful to David Baker, who wrote the chapters on barrel blueing and browning, and to Geoff Worrall of Tideline Books who read the manuscript in draft and made numerous helpful suggestions. The proof regulations are reproduced by kind permission of the Birmingham Proof House. Certain photographs are reproduced by kind permission of *Sporting Gun* magazine.

CHAPTER ONE

Introduction

Having worked in the gun trade for many years, it never ceases to surprise me how little care and attention some shooters give their guns.

Perhaps I am a little too fastidious, but I like to think not. There are of course thousands of people who give their guns all the attention and care needed. Some give them too much 'care' – the 'oil can addicts' are a prime example of this. They seem to think that as long as a gun gets plenty of oil in regular large doses, it will repay the gesture with a lifetime's trouble-free service. Alas this is not always the case, since too much oil will normally result in a fault of some sort developing. Oil attracts dirt as jam attracts bees! So while you need a little to keep moving parts working smoothly, and to keep rust at bay, be sparing in its use.

Similarly, some seem to have an obsession about smothering the surface of the stock with various concoctions. That is fine if you want to end up with sticky, unsightly woodwork on your gun – but definitely not otherwise.

Gun care, like most other things in life, is all things in moderation. Clean your gun regularly, always after use, but avoid too much tinkering and use of the oil can.

Every now and then however your gun will need completely stripping and cleaning. This is a necessary function that ensures its safe and smooth operation – it also helps maintain its value. On average a gun needs to be stripped and cleaned at least once every two years. This enables a visual inspection of all the working parts to take place giving the opportunity to discover if anything is badly worn, cracked or even broken. Whilst certain skills are required to carry out this operation, it is not beyond the ability of the average practically minded sportsman, particularly one with an engineering background.

A few simple rules need to be observed and careful consideration must be given before starting the task. A logical and methodical approach should be used and both the text and photographs which follow need to be studied carefully. It is easier to make a mistake than to rectify one, and if you are the type who likes to get things done in a hurry, then you'll either need to undergo a personality change or abandon the whole idea of doing your own gun repairs.

I am quite sure that most people can easily follow the process but I do want to stress the importance of literally taking it *one step at a time*. I am equally sure you will find it a fascinating process discovering the mysteries of a gun and what causes it to go bang at the squeeze of a trigger.

Although it takes many years of exacting training (coupled with a dedication to detail and an inbuilt pride of workmanship) to become a gunmaker, the stripping of a gun is but a small, although very necessary, part of the gunmaker's craft. Confidence in one's own ability is a prime factor and complete mastery of one's tools is a must.

CHAPTER TWO

The Workbench

Before you attempt to do any work on your gun, it is important that you not only have the right tools and materials but also a properly equipped workbench.

With the help of a few simple attachments, an ordinary bench can be transformed to lend itself to almost any kind of gun repair that you are likely to wish to undertake. Yet without those attachments you could do your gun more harm than good.

A bench rest is of vital importance. This must be able to pivot freely. If wood is chosen, a hole drilled through the end of the rest and the bench top will allow for a suitable nut and bolt to be fitted.

A simple version can also be made from a ³/₄″ round bar of steel or, alternatively, tubular 'conduit' piping. The portion that supports the wood needs to be filed flat so that the wood can be attached firmly by means of two wood screws passing through the metal and into the wood.

A collar is attached to the leg of the rest by means of a small threaded locking screw. When slackened this will allow the rest to be raised or lowered as required. A clearance size hole needs to be drilled into the bench top to accommodate the leg which can then be swung into position or out of the way.

To protect the stock against damage, the rest needs to be covered with padding, using either a cloth wrapped around it or layers of thick felt. When soiled or worn this should be replaced.

The rest is positioned next to the vice so that the stock can be supported comfortably and safely at about the same height as the top of the vice. It is wiser to have a rest on each side of the vice – this makes working on both sides of a stock much easier.

It has often been said that a bad workman blames his tools but what you don't generally hear about is the fact that the good workman will usually have excellent tools, kept in first-class order. He will also ensure that he has the right conditions and facilities in which to work.

Protecting your normal clothing from the inevitable oil and dirt of gun work is obviously a good idea. The traditional white cotton apron obtainable from most decorating shops is perfectly adequate except that it fails to protect the clothing under the armpits. This is where the stock is held when 'breaking' the gun to test the action or ejectors or when fitting the barrels to the action. A proper gunmaker's apron has sides which reach up to and fit

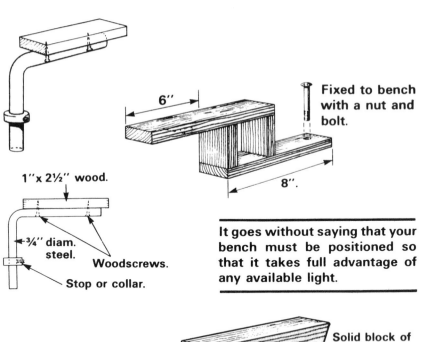

6"

Fixed to bench with a nut and bolt.

8".

1" x 2½" wood.

¾" diam. steel.

Woodscrews.

Stop or collar.

It goes without saying that your bench must be positioned so that it takes full advantage of any available light.

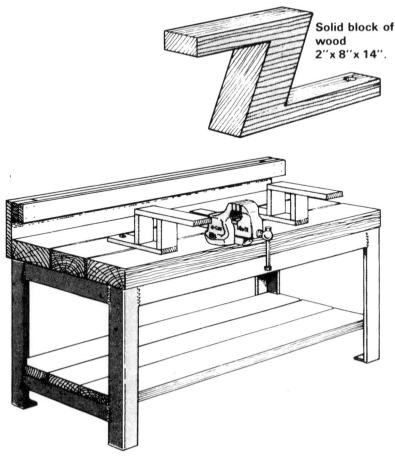

Solid block of wood 2" x 8" x 14".

snugly into the armpits. It extends down to just below the knees. About two square yards of fairly stout white cotton 'duck' or canvas is normally sufficient with a few yards of white tape.

The drawing shows where the tapes are attached. Those at the top are fixed permanently and are slipped over the head crossing at the back. The waist tapes should be long enough to pass once around the back and tie in a bow at the front. Both sets of tapes should be pinned temporarily in place, to try out for length and comfort, then sewn securely. A breast pocket, to hold pencils and small items, can be added and a split 'lap' pocket will be found useful for larger items. The dotted lines on the drawing indicate where the sides of an ordinary paperhanger's apron extend to.

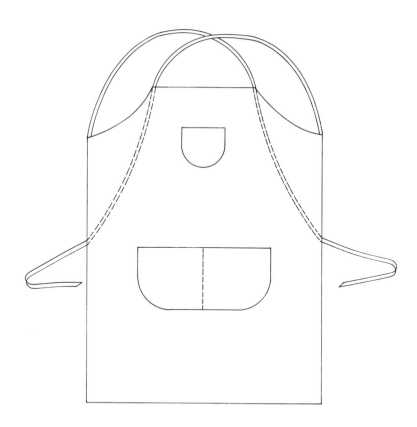

In the case of gun maintenance and repair, the general run-of-the-mill stockwork or action cleaning does not demand the greatest number of tools nor the most expensive accessories available, but the provision of a properly equipped workbench is invaluable.

I hope the illustrations and my brief descriptions give the detail you require.

The list of tools needed is relatively small. Your shopping list should include the following:

Oil and cloth: A clean piece of cloth, preferably cotton, plus a can of 3-in-1 (or similar) oil. I also use white Vaseline to smear on certain parts after cleaning.

Feathers: Wing and tail feathers of pigeon, partridge or pheasant are ideal for cleaning difficult holes and corners.

Shaped piece of wood: A piece of wood size 7″ × ¼″ × 1½″ and shaped to allow access into the slot on the body of the action for removal of the hammer. See photograph of tools on the right.

Wooden dowel: A piece of dowel measuring 5″ long and thinned down to allow access into the slot on the action body.

Main spring clamp: This is essential for compressing and releasing the springs on a sidelock and can be purchased for under £20. The model I use came from Peter Dyson of Huddersfield (as did the turnscrews).

Turnscrews: A basic set of three gunmakers' turnscrews (screwdrivers) are needed. They should be hollow ground (using an oval file).

Pin punches: Three of various sizes are needed. I suggest ⅛″, ³/₃₂″ and ¼″. They can be bought at your local tool shop for about £1 each.

Hammer: A small flat pein type, weighing about ½ lb.

Engineer's vice: A standard workshop model with 4½″ jaws which obviously needs to be mounted on a secure bench.

Vice guards: Made from scraps of aluminium or lead and measuring 2½″ wide. They need to be the length of the vice and folded at 90 degrees. If you can't get hold of some scrap pieces, as an alternative DIY measure simply cut open an empty beer can, and remove top and bottom.

Parts box: Often called a stripping box, an empty cigar or cardboard box is ideal for placing each part in as it is removed.

Snap caps: These are needed to check that the firing pins and ejectors work correctly when reassembled.

Spring clamp lever: Made from a piece of scrap mild steel measuring ½″ × ⅛″, and 6″ long. Cut a slot in one end with a hacksaw.

1. Desmond Mills pictured in his workshop holding a Churchill boxlock.

2. The tools you will need to strip and clean your gun.

1.   Desmond Mills at a corner of his workbench – you will not be needing quite so many files!

CHAPTER THREE

Turnscrews and Vice Jaws

If you have been fortunate enough to have visited a proper gunmaker's workshop it is almost certain that you were impressed by the number and variety of tools on his bench. The majority would certainly have been hand files of various shapes, sizes and cut, in some cases used to carry out only one small operation on the building or repair of a shotgun.

The turnscrew is possibly the most frequently used of all his tools and certainly one of the most important. But, before I go any farther, I should perhaps explain that in gunmakers' parlance a screwdriver is called a turnscrew and a screw is often known as a 'pin'.

Most gunmakers make their own turnscrews. It is usual for them to be made during the early years of one's apprenticeship; my own were, and are still in use today. The gunmaker needs a large, varied selection to enable him to undertake the work on many different models of gun, whilst the DIY shooter will possibly require only three or perhaps four different sizes. In certain cases the turnscrew is only required to do one specific job: for example, the breech or body pin requires the largest one in his selection.

Certain basic fundamentals must be followed before any attempt is made to remove a 'pin'. The most important part of the turnscrew is the blade for, unlike the conventional screwdriver as used by joiners and electricians, the gunmakers' turnscrew is shorter in length and rather differently shaped.

When attempting to remove a pin, no matter what size it may be, the same procedure must be adopted every time.

The turnscrew should have a hollow ground blade. The width of the blade must be less than that of the pin or screw slot. Last but of no less importance, is complete control of the turnscrew, if you wish to avoid damage to the slots in the heads of the pins. We have all seen examples of guns whose pins have been mutilated and have the look of having been removed by means of a chisel or blunt instrument. The rims of the holes may be scored, slots deformed, part of the head broken off, in some cases the pin has been forced open – ugly sights indeed and certainly an eyesore when looking at what once was neat professional work!

Perhaps we should look a little deeper into what is required to remove tight pins and at the same time retain the crispness of their slots. The hollow ground blade is achieved by holding the turnscrew in the vice and filing it to shape by using a six-inch oval hand file. It is essential that the blade enter the slot of the pin as far as possible, thus enabling you to obtain the maximum purchase with your turnscrew.

If we consider a conventional screwdriver blade, it is wedge-shaped to fit many different types of slot and the tendency is to bear only on a very small area of the sides of the slot. This tends to force or wedge the head of the pin apart on being pressed into the slot.

Always try to ensure that the full weight of one's body is directly over the handle of the turnscrew. Taking a firm grip, the shoulder should be in line with the blade to obtain the maximum amount of purchase and so remove any danger of the blade slipping and scratching metal or woodwork.

The length of blade and the shape of handle is purely a matter of personal choice. There are no hard-and-fast rules, as the individual's hand varies in size and strength. The user must be comfortable when gripping the handle, although a very short blade prevents the user seeing what he is doing properly.

Although the blade of the turnscrew has been heat treated (hardened and tempered), do not be afraid to 'dress' (reshape) the blade with a file several times if needing to work on different-size pins. You must guard against the temptation to 'make do' with a poorly fitting blade when only one screw needs to be slackened or tightened. Taking short cuts, due to impatience, is a sure recipe for disaster. Reshaping the blade on an electric grindstone will overheat it and soften the point, causing it either to twist out of shape or wear out quickly.

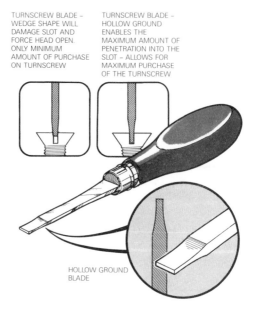

TURNSCREW BLADE – WEDGE SHAPE WILL DAMAGE SLOT AND FORCE HEAD OPEN. ONLY MINIMUM AMOUNT OF PURCHASE ON TURNSCREW

TURNSCREW BLADE – HOLLOW GROUND ENABLES THE MAXIMUM AMOUNT OF PENETRATION INTO THE SLOT – ALLOWS FOR MAXIMUM PURCHASE OF THE TURNSCREW

HOLLOW GROUND BLADE

For the benefit of beginners, I should explain that when using your workbench, protection for the jaws of the vice is a must!

The standard engineer's vice is fitted with extremely hard, serrated jaws which will bite into and disfigure the metal of your gun. Protection of the jaws can be carried out in several ways at little or no cost. While many gunmakers have special thick lead guards to fit the jaws of the vice, a good DIY substitute is to use two pieces of at least $1/16''$-thick sheet aluminium, measuring about $2''$ wide by $4^1/2''$ or so long and bent at 90 degrees. Alternatively fibre or felt vice guards can be purchased from many tool merchants at a modest price.

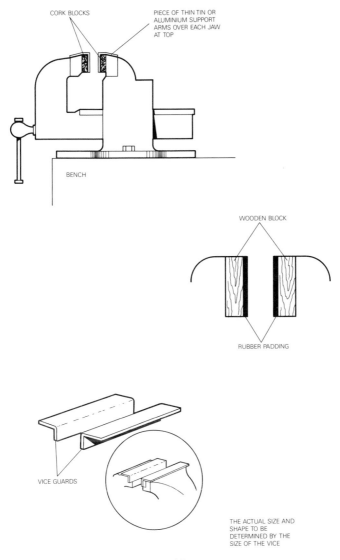

CORK BLOCKS

PIECE OF THIN TIN OR
ALUMINIUM SUPPORT
ARMS OVER EACH JAW
AT TOP

BENCH

WOODEN BLOCK

RUBBER PADDING

VICE GUARDS

THE ACTUAL SIZE AND
SHAPE TO BE
DETERMINED BY THE
SIZE OF THE VICE

2. A standard workshop bench with aluminium shields.

For emergencies only, the cheapest method involves using an empty aluminium soft-drinks can. Remove both the top and bottom using tin snips or an old pair of scissors (not your wife's best dressmaking scissors or you will be in trouble!), cut the can completely in half lengthways and hammer flat using a block of wood or mallet. Place one half in the vice and bend the other half to 90 degrees. Repeat the operation for the other vice jaw. It is essential first to remove all sharp and jagged edges with a file or rough emery cloth, or you may be badly cut.

Lead, aluminium or fibre is ideal for holding the action or small metal parts, although special care must be taken when holding the action. Close the vice jaws gently but firmly otherwise you could apply too much pressure to the vice handle and accidentally squeeze the action in. You will then be unable to fit the barrels to the action – a major disaster!

If the stock needs to be held in the vice, then we need to consider another material: cork is ideal or thick pads of felt. Usually decorating merchants sell cork pads for use in sanding down woodwork which can be sawn to shape.

CHAPTER FOUR

The Boxlock

The gun I have chosen to illustrate the job in hand is a Churchill 12 bore boxlock ejector. The reason for this choice is purely because the Churchill is not only a good gun, but is also a prime example of an Anson & Deeley boxlock, the most popular style of side-by-side action to be found both in the UK and worldwide.

I have chosen an emphasis on visual presentation for this step-by-step guide as I am sure that for a technical operation such as this, it is the easiest method to follow.

Give yourself plenty of time, make sure your workshop bench is absolutely clear and concentrate on the job in hand. Here endeth the first lesson!

As pointed out, all screwdrivers are referred to as turnscrews – if you are going to do the job you might as well be professional about it. The turnscrews themselves will need to be kept sharp and hollow ground. This can be achieved by using an oval file or half round file to dress the end of the turnscrew as needed. The most important point to bear in mind is that the turnscrew must be narrower in width than the actual pin (all screws are referred to as pins) that is to be removed. Conversely the fit should not be sloppy either (see illustration). If the turnscrew doesn't fit properly it can slip out and damage the gun.

The actions of virtually all guns are precision made and it should never be a struggle to remove parts. Occasionally you will find tight pins, but if you encounter serious difficulties you are doing something wrong. Don't force the issue – you will only bend, strain or break something. Stop, think and check what you have done against the pictures and instructions.

As each part is removed a visual examination should be carried out to see if any parts are badly worn, or indeed if any cracks or breakages have occurred or are about to occur. If you do notice that anything is amiss have no hesitation in taking your gun to a recognised gunsmith. Finding a fault at this stage should be a source of pride, and will almost certainly avoid a situation of embarrassment (or worse) in the shooting field.

One final point to remember is that when you come to oil or Vaseline the parts on replacement, most people are far too generous with lubrication. Excess can lead to an unnecessary picking up of grit and dirt, that can in turn undo all your good work and risk damaging your gun. The emphasis is on a light application.

1, 2.   To start the operation remove the fore-end and detach the barrels. Your first job is to remove the extractor retaining pin usually found on the front lump. You will see from the picture that the method of releasing the pin is by bringing your shoulder (and weight) directly over the turnscrew. The reason for this is to bring the maximum purchase on your turnscrew in order to slacken the pin. Once slackened the pin can be unscrewed in the normal manner – it is vital that all pins are treated similarly, thus greatly reducing the risk of your turnscrew going astray from the job in hand and damaging your gun.

3, 4.   Having removed the retaining pin from the front lump you can now slide out the extractors (ejectors). A common place for a crack or fault to occur is at the bottom of one of the legs.

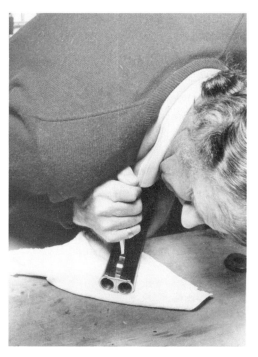

1

2

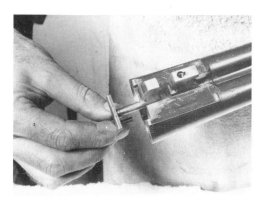

3

4

15

5.   This picture shows the dirt on the extractors – always a problem area for both dirt and water. Wipe them clean with a rag.

6.   Now it's time for the feather, an extremely practical piece of cleaning equipment. All pin holes, slots and corners are easily cleaned by the insertion and working of a feather. And don't forget the extractor hole between the barrels.

7.   Methods vary but I always clean the insides of the barrels themselves with a wire brush screwed onto the end of a conventional cleaning rod. A little oil is placed onto the brush itself and the rod is then inserted into the barrels from the muzzle end. Pull it through (never push it up) and it will keep its shape – the one I use is 20 years old and nearly as good now as when I bought it.

Then remove the wire brush and replace with a nylon jag, wire loop (or similar) and attach a piece of clean, soft cloth, rag or conventional cleaning patch. The rod is then inserted from the breech end to remove oil and dirt.

However, a safer option than the wire brush may be to use a hog's bristle brush, nylon filament or phosphor bronze wire brush.

Misused, a 'turks head' or steel wire brush can easily scratch your barrels – a lot of care must be taken. However, this brush is especially useful for the occasional removal of very stubborn 'leading', i.e., traces of pellet lead left at breech or chokes.

If purchasing a set of cleaning equipment from your local gunshop you will normally find that in addition to a two- or three-joint wooden rod, the kit will contain a hog's bristle or phosphor bronze brush, a nylon jag or wire loop to take a cleaning patch and a wool mop for oiling or polishing the bore. These are ideal for the job.

Give the outside of the barrels a light wipe over with oil and your first step of the operation is now complete. All you have to do at this stage now is to put the extractors back into the barrel after giving them a light smear with white Vaseline, and then replace the extractor pin. Don't put any weight on it until the final turn when you should once again get your shoulder directly above the turnscrew. It is only on that last turn that any pressure is necessary – it should screw in easily until that point.

You can now put the barrels to one side – perhaps in your gun rack or case.

5

6

7

8, 9, 10, 11.   Prior to starting, ensure the gun is in the cocked position. First we remove the trigger guard. Turn the stock upside-down and place the face of the action over the edge of your workbench, holding it firmly in place with pressure being applied by your body on the end of the stock. As at all times, make sure you are in full control and that the gun is completely secure. Supporting the stock with the left hand select your turnscrew, ensuring that it fits snugly into the pin to be removed, and place into the head of the pin. As explained earlier the method of slackening all pins is to bring your shoulder and weight directly over the turnscrew – and that the chances of it slipping out and damaging your gun are slight.

Remember each part should be examined carefully for dirt, damage, breakage or wear before being placed in the stripping box (don't put any parts to one side – always make sure they go in the box).

Now place the thumb of the left hand into the front of the trigger guard, gently pushing forward. The tail of the trigger guard will lift up and is then normally removed by unscrewing in an anti-clockwise direction.

8

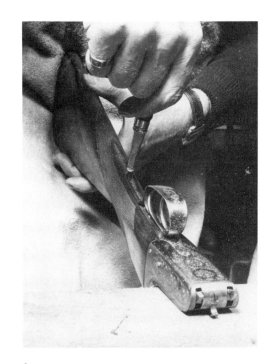

9

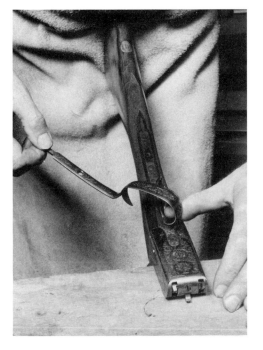

10

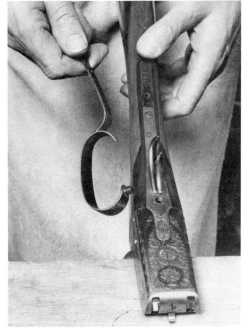

11

12.   And now we come to the nitty-gritty – the mechanism of your gun.

We first remove the bottom plate by slackening the pin shown and using the same method as on the first pin of the trigger guard.

13, 14.   Having removed the pin, turn the action the correct way up with the fingers of the hand supporting the bottom plate. Gently tap with a piece of dowel to release the bottom plate from the action.

15.   Now at last we can begin to see the insides of the gun and discover just how much dirt has accumulated.

16.   The gun's conventional Anson & Deeley action. We are now seeing some of the craftsman's skills that go into the building of a shotgun. As the gun is further stripped down so the quality of workmanship becomes more apparent.

12

13 14

15

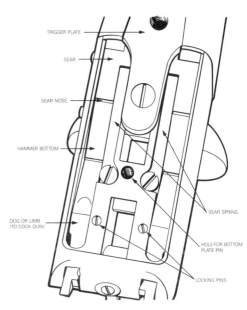

TRIGGER PLATE

SEAR

SEAR NOSE

HAMMER BOTTOM

DOG OR LIMB
(TO COCK GUN)

SEAR SPRING

HOLE FOR BOTTOM
PLATE PIN

LOCKING PINS

16

17. Our next objective is to remove the trigger plate. Hold the small of the stock in the left hand, and place the bottom of the action on the bench while at the same time holding the top lever open with your thumb, thus revealing the head of the breech pin. At this stage we merely wish to release the breech pin by half a turn. This is the biggest and tightest pin on the gun – give it plenty of respect.

18. Turn the action upside-down again in order to slacken the trigger plate pin and the hand pin. The hand pin (the one at the top of the plate) goes right the way through the hand of the stock.

Turn the gun the correct way up once again (see inset) and remove the breech pin.

19. Turn the action upside-down again. Remove the trigger plate pin and finally the hand pin which passes completely through the small of the stock.

17

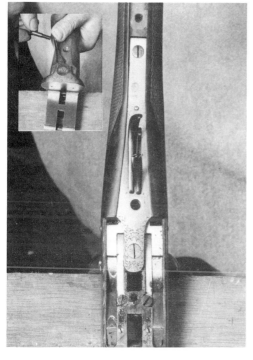

18

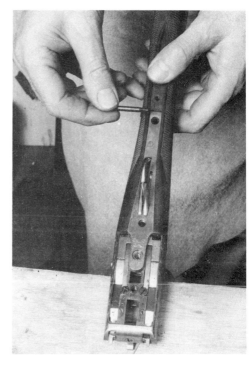

19

20.   Still keeping the action face down on the edge of the work bench, supporting the stock with the left hand, gently proceed to loosen and lift the trigger plate out of the stock.

21.   The trigger plate removed, showing the safety slide in the 'safe' position.

22.   Having taken the trigger plate off, turn the gun to the upright position so that the gun is held securely in place under your left arm and the small of the stock supported in the left hand. Hold the body of the action in the right hand and gently remove from the stock. The stock should now be placed in a safe place so as not to mark or damage the wood. Prior to doing this you should, of course, carry out a visual inspection to see if the head of the stock (where it fits against the rear of the action body) is cracked or even split.

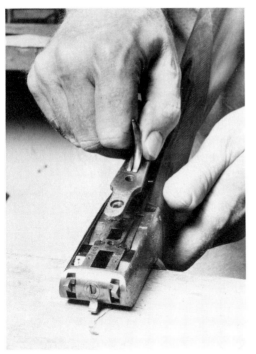

20

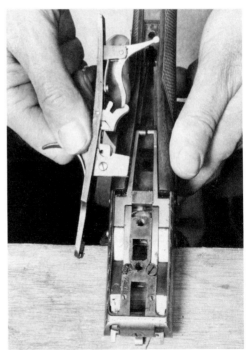

21

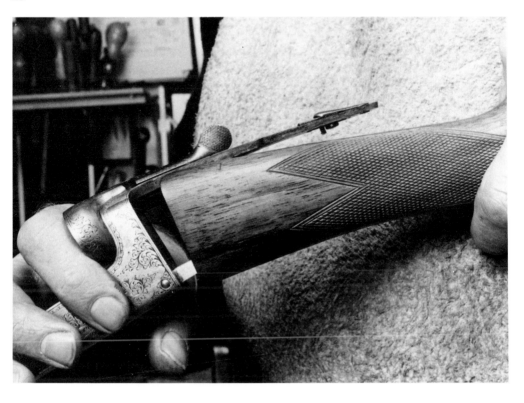

22

23.   This illustration shows the action and the reassembled trigger plate after the removal of the stock merely to show the position of the breech pin, hand pin and safety mechanism. There is no need for you to do this – unless you want to satisfy your curiosity.

24.   Our next task is to remove all of the inside work of the action and our first job is to uncock both hammers. Turn the action upside-down and hold in your left hand firmly against the edge of the bench. Take a piece of dowel, press gently onto the bottom of the left-hand hammer and release the sear by pressing carefully with your left thumb. All the time the dowel should be held down firmly with the right hand so as to maintain control of the firing mechanism and slowly releasing the hammer itself. Releasing the spring too quickly could result in a broken spring! Repeat the same operation to the right hammer so that they are now both uncocked. Both hammers will now be in the forward or fired position.

25, 26.   This picture shows the action from underneath and the hammers in a fired position, i.e., flat with no tension. The sears however are still under tension. Prior to their removal the sear springs must first of all be released – these are quite simply a strip of metal on the inside of each sear. The arrow on the picture, No. 26, shows where one spring has been removed. This was done by the removal of the pin at its head.

27.   Removal of the sears can now take place. This is where the vice guards come into use, so as not to damage the action which is at this stage placed in the vice, where it is held gently but securely. Select the appropriate pin punch and carefully tap the end of the pin (in this case smooth with no thread) which retains the sears within the action, guiding the pin with the left hand out of the body of the action.

28.   Supporting both sears, remove the pin punch.

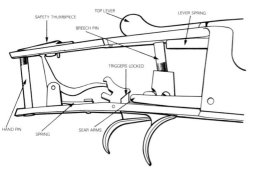

23

24

25

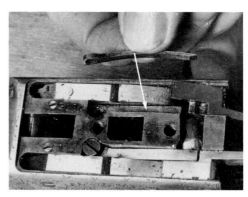

26

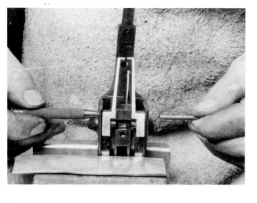

27

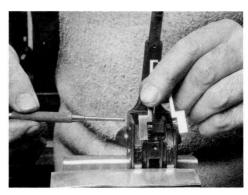

28

29.   At this point it may be worth while replacing the pin into the two sears before placing in the box. Note the dirt, and also the marks on the pin to differentiate from other pins within the action, and the correct side to insert the pin from. Check also the nose of the sears to make sure they have not become rounded – this could be the cause of excessively light or inexplicably variable trigger pulls. But if one or both are worn, rounded or chipped, don't attempt to rectify them yourself. You have done well to spot the fault. Setting up and regulating trigger pulls is an important and highly specialised job which should not be attempted by the amateur. Simply make a note at this stage, carry on with the stripping, cleaning and reassembly of your gun, then take it to your local gunsmith informing him of the fault (plus any others you may find).

30, 31.   The safety thumb piece is removed simply by the release of the pin.

29

30

31

32 to 43. The first part we look at is the lever spring. Turning the action upside-down the lever spring is clearly visible sitting on the underneath of the strap (some people refer to this as the tang of the action).

You will now need your spring clamp lever (the piece of metal with a slot cut in one end). Take the action in your left hand, and push the top lever open to its full extent, to compress the spring and enable the spring clamp lever to slot into place over it.

Keeping your thumb firmly in place lift the spring out of its housing. Put the action to one side for a moment, take a piece of cloth in your left hand and wrapping it over the clamp and spring, remove the spring from the clamp. There is a lot of tension on the spring, and by using the cloth in this way you curb the spring's natural inclination to fly off into the furthest corner of the room!

Rest the action flat on the top of the bench, hold the strap and top lever with your left hand and place the appropriate turnscrew in the slot of the lever pin.

This pin can now be completely removed.

Take the action in your left hand, holding it close to your body with the strap pointing away. You will see from the picture that it is important that the top lever is held firmly in the closed position. Having selected the smallest diameter pin punch place it into the hole vacated by the top lever pin. The reason for using the smallest diameter punch is to avoid damaging the thread of the spindle. The pin punch is gently tapped with the hammer so as to release the

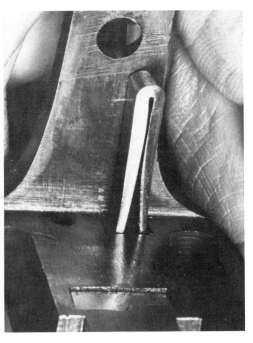

32

33

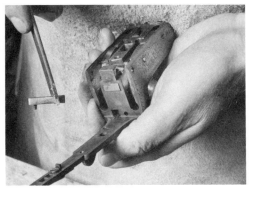

34

35

36

37

spindle from the top lever and the bolt (see Fig. 39 and 40).

Now turn the action upside-down and withdraw the spindle with the right hand. The end of the bolt on this gun juts out slightly – this is not always the case.

The next step is the withdrawal of the bolt. This might be slack and slip out easily on the removal of the spindle. Alternatively it might be a tight fit (most likely as a result of being slightly dirty), in which case it has to be edged out. If you can't get a grip of it at its end, place the piece of wooden dowel into the back slot (the rectangular hole in the centre of the base of the action) and gently lift the bolt so as to ease it.

When a gun is closed the bolt (Fig. 42 inset) locks the barrels to the action by sliding forward approximately one eighth of an inch. In this way it moves into the bites of the barrels (see Fig. 41) and so grips them in place.

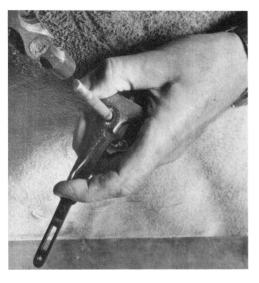

38

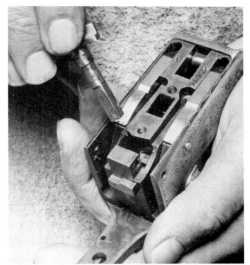

39

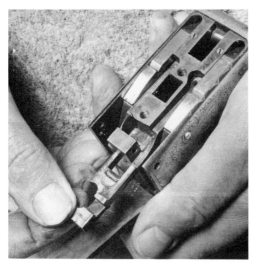

40

41

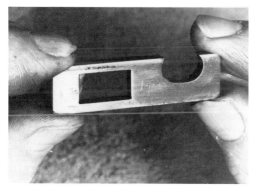

42

43 to 46. Fig. 43 shows how the top lever, spindle and bolt all fit and work together inside the gun.

We now want to remove the limbs from the action and in order to do this our first step is to unscrew the locking pins. In the photograph (Fig. 44) one of the pins has already been removed, and the other is partly removed. You may find that your gun does not have locking pins. Don't worry – this is common with many boxlocks. Some have them – some don't.

Now place the action on its side and having selected the appropriate turnscrew remove the pins on either side of the front end of the action. Check that there is a marking of some sort on the pin, so that you don't confuse the left- and right-hand pins when you come to putting the gun back together. If they are not marked, simply make a small scratch on the left one so that you can immediately differentiate between it and the other.

Fig. 46 shows how the locking pin (for those guns that have them) operates.

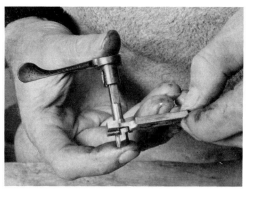

43

44

45

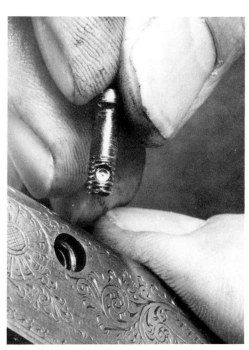

46

47 to 52. The second of the two limbs is here (Fig. 47) being lifted out of the action. Fig. 48 shows a side view of the limb.

We now come to possibly the most difficult part of the whole operation – the removal of the hammers. Fig. 49 shows both the hammers and the main springs.

Make sure that the aluminium vice guards are placed in the vice, and clamp the action as shown in the photograph. Select your pin punch (again slightly smaller than the hole) and gently tap the pin approximately halfway through (see Fig. 50 – removed from vice only for purposes of this article). We are removing the right-hand hammer and spring first.

Still retaining the action in the vice take the shaped piece of wood in your right hand and push against the base of the hammer. The hammer is still in the fired position so apply pressure with the piece of wood pushing upwards and in an anti-clockwise movement. With the wood held firmly against the base of the hammer you can now withdraw your pin punch.

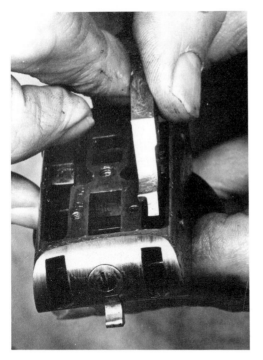

47

48

49

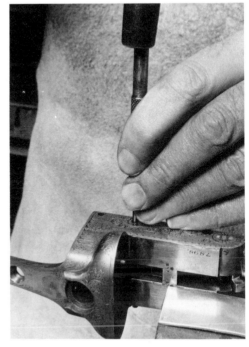

50

On no account attempt to remove the pin punch without the base of the hammer being under tension (i.e. with the use of the wood). If you do, this could result in a nasty accident. The main spring is extremely powerful.

53.   Gently withdraw the piece of wood thus allowing the hammer to come out of the action and releasing the pressure on the main spring. With the piece of wood firmly held you have complete control. So you must make sure that your stance is good and that you are master of the job in hand.

54 shows the hammer coming out.

With the hammer removed the main spring is no longer under compression and hangs out of the bottom of the action, and can now also be removed simply with thumb and forefinger (55).

56 shows how the spring and hammer sit in the action.

We now have to remove the left-hand hammer and main spring, so the next step is to turn the action upside-down and place in the other end of the vice (again with the aluminium guards in place). The pin which has been knocked through from the other side by the punch will be protruding.

Gently tap the pin down with the hammer until it is level with the other side of the action. Take your pin punch and proceed to drive the pin through the action so it comes out the other side. You can now repeat the same operation with the piece of wood to remove the left-hand hammer and main spring.

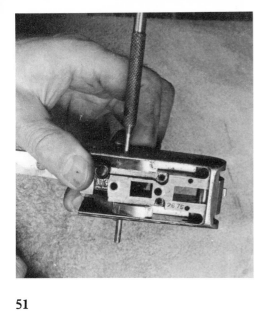

51

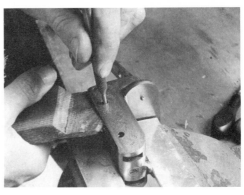

52

53

54

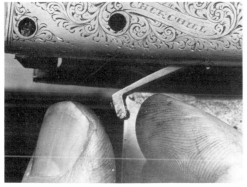

55

56

57.   This shows the left-hand hammer and main spring. Note the
scratch marks on both, which indicate that they are from the
left-hand side of the action. There will be no mark on the right-side
parts.

58.   It's all there somewhere! The stripping down is complete, and
all the parts are in the box.

   Your gun has been stripped for a purpose – to check and clean it. So now,
as we make ready to reassemble it, we must look closely at each individual
part, cleaning, oiling and making sure there is nothing amiss. If you spot a
crack, wear or damage, make a note of it, then follow the step-by-step guide
to re-assembly before taking the gun to your gunsmith to tell him of the
problem.
   The exercise is purely to clean your gun and give you a more intimate
knowledge of the way it works.

59 to 61.   All pin holes, threaded or otherwise, can be cleaned
easily and effectively with a feather.

62.   Place a piece of rag on the end of a narrow file to enable you
to gain access into the slots and remove any dirt, grit or foreign
matter.

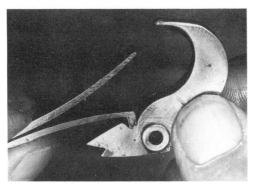

57

58

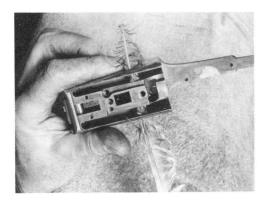

59

60

61

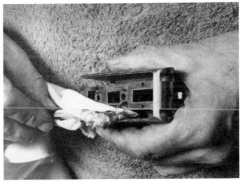

62

63, 64.   Re-assembly is not a straight reversal of the stripping process. There isn't a strict order of work, but over the years I have found it best to start re-assembly with the lever work. Remember, while oil and grease are essential, both are to be used sparingly. If you use to excess you defeat the object. Simply make sure that each part is wiped and cleaned, applying a thin smearing of oil or grease. Start reassembly by placing the top lever in the lever hole.

65.   Having turned the action upside down, hold it in your left hand and replace the bolt, first giving it a thin smear of grease. Make sure the bolt is pushed fully home.

66.   Still with the action upside down in your left hand, put a light smear of grease on the spindle (especially on the squares). Make sure that the top lever is in the central position on the strap of the action, and insert the spindle into the spindle hole. It should be pushed in as far as possible.

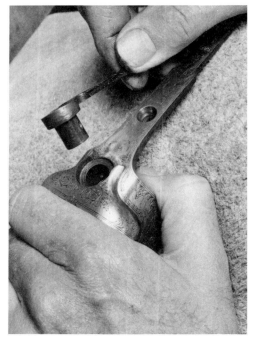

63

64

65

66

67.   Making sure that the vice guards are in place, open the vice to approximately 1½″ wide, place the action on the vice as shown. With the punch (as illustrated) gently tap home the spindle. The punch in the picture obviously isn't in use, it is merely pointing to the head of the spindle now in place. Remove from the vice.

68, 69.   The next operation is to insert the top lever pin, which you will notice has an angled head in order to sit flush with the lever itself. The inset picture shows the cleaning and greasing of pins.

70.   Holding the action with your left hand (with the top lever in the closed position) flat on the bench, put your weight over the lever pin to apply the final turn which will make it lie flush.

71.   Now take the lever spring and insert in the edge of the vice with the aluminium guards in position. Compress the spring as shown in the photograph.

67

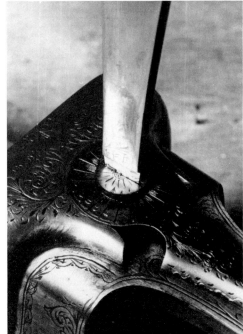

68

69

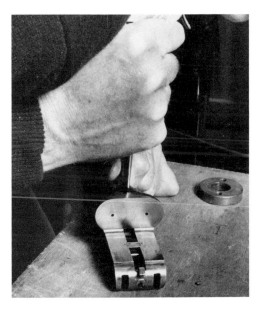

70

71

72.   Insert the spring clamp over the spring, and then gently release the vice with the other hand. The spring will now hold itself in the clamp.

73.   Turning the action upside-down again, supporting it in your left hand with the lever pushed fully open insert the closed spring into the hole.

74.   Allow the lever to come to the closed position, then place your thumb on the end of the spring and remove your clamp.

75.   Of the two main springs, select the one with the scratch which indicates left-hand side, smear with grease and slot into the action.

76.   This photograph shows the main spring back in place.

77.   We now place the hammer back in its working position on the spring.

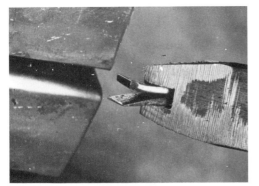

72

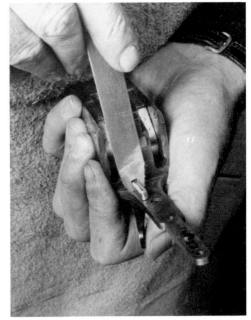

73

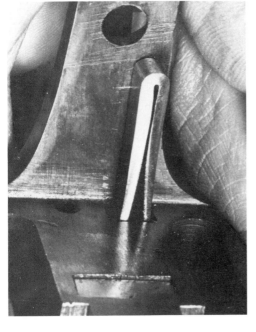

74

75

76

77

78.   Make sure that the action is properly secure in the vice, take the piece of wood in your right hand and place on the base of the hammer, turning (and pressing) the wood in a clockwise manner. The end of the striker will protrude through the striker hole in the face of the action and will allow you to insert your pin punch. Leave the punch in the action, thus keeping the hammer in the fired position.

We can now remove the piece of wood.

Remove the action from the vice, and hold it in your left hand with the pin punch pointing down. Take the smooth pin (whose work the pin punch is at present undertaking) and place in the hole immediately opposite the pin punch.

79.   Gently tap it, so pushing the punch out. Now place the action back in the vice, so as to enable the same operation to be conducted on the right-hand side, i.e., the punch will have tapped into the right-hand side to push the pin just over halfway through. Remove the punch and insert the right-hand main spring and hammer. Engage the hammer and spring with the piece of wood as before.

Having pushed the hammer up into a fired position, again using the piece of wood with pressure firmly applied, insert the pin punch.

80.   This shows both sides in place, but one still being held by the punch. Gently tap the end of the pin so as to remove the punch and both hammers will now be retained.

Having cleaned and checked the action and replaced the lever work, hammers and the main springs, the next step is to replace the two limbs.

78

79

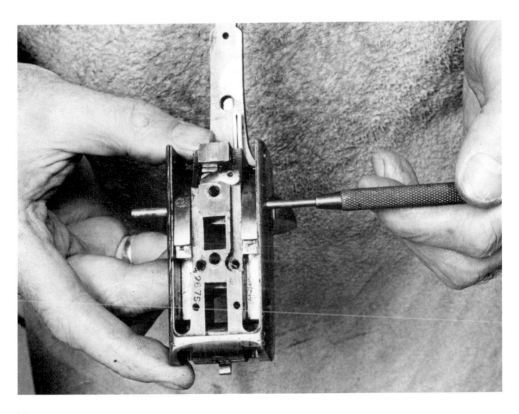

80

81, 82.   We are replacing the left-hand side first, but it matters little which one you select.

83.   Having put the two limbs in place, each retained by a pin, the left-hand one is distinguished by a mark across its bottom end. In this picture the locking pin is replaced – your gun may not have one of these.

84.   The next job is to replace the sears – make sure they are wiped perfectly clean. The picture shows the kind of dirt they can gather. Remember after cleaning to smear lightly with oil or Vaseline.

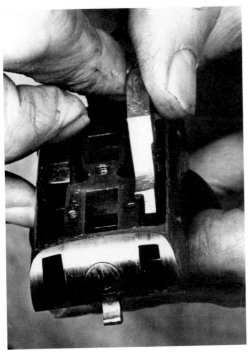

81

82

83

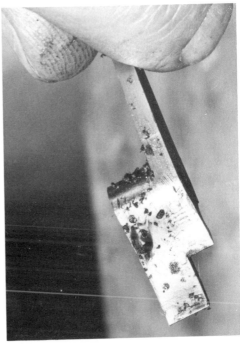

84

85.   Holding the action in your left hand, place the right-hand sear into the bottom of the action, select the small pin punch and insert into the hole in the action in order to retain the sear. Push approximately halfway in. Then replace the left-hand sear, lining up the hole in the sear with the end of the pin punch so as to enable the punch to pass right through the body of the action, as shown in the photograph.

86.   We now remove the pin punch by withdrawing and replacing with the original pin. This is a reversal of the process we used in stripping the gun, the pin punch being used as guide so that the pin passes through the holes in the two sears.

87.   You will notice now that the sears are not under tension, so our next task is to replace the sear springs (see Fig. 19). Holding the action in your left hand (with your forefinger under the sear arms to prevent the sear dropping backwards), place the right-hand sear spring in position and secure with the appropriate pin. Adopt the same procedure for the left-hand side.

88.   The next operation is to cock the gun. Place the action on the edge of bench as shown, holding in the left hand and depressing the right-hand sear with thumb. Take the piece of dowel in the right hand and press down on the base of the hammer. This will compress the main spring and allow the nose of the sear to sit in the bent of the hammer. Gently remove the dowel and repeat the same operation on the other sear.

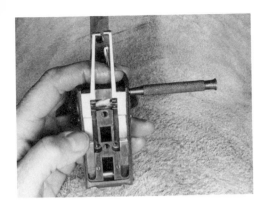

85

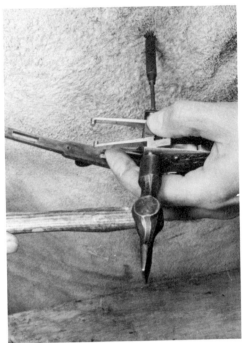

86

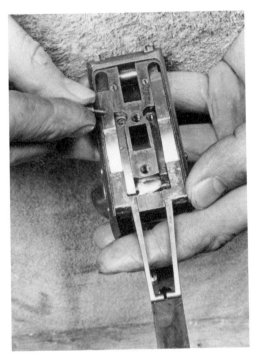

87

88

89. This photograph shows the hammers now in the cocked position.

90. Replace the safety thumb piece screw, and the safety slide.

91, 92. Taking the action in the right hand, the small of the stock in the left hand holding it close to the body, gently ease the action into the head of the stock taking care not to damage the woodwork.

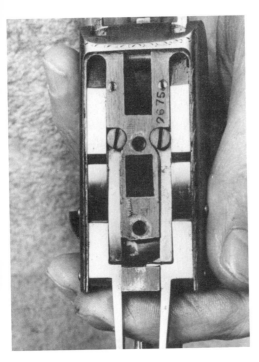

89

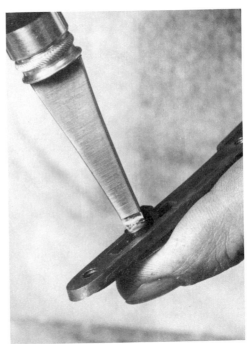

90

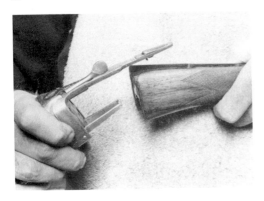

91

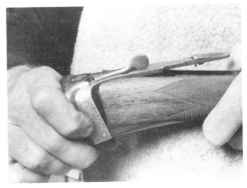

92

93.   Turning the action upside down and placing the face of the action on the edge of the bench, and the heel of the stock against your stomach (if you have not had a light lunch you might now regret it!) take the trigger plate, as shown in the photograph, and gently slot into place. While doing this you must make sure that the safety thumb piece is in the safe position. And of course that the trigger work is clean.

94.   Select the thicker of the two pins (this would normally be the trigger plate pin).

95.   Insert the trigger plate pin, but don't turn it fully home at this stage.

96.   Replace the hand pin, again not fully home.

93

94

95

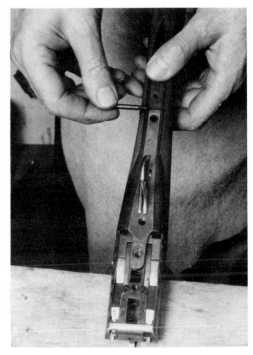

96

97.   Turn the action upright, hold in the left hand with the lever fully open, and insert the breech pin.

98.   Placing the base of the action on the bench, still holding the lever back with the thumb, and using the correct turnscrew, turn the breech pin fully home. Remember when turning pins tightly that you should always have your weight directly over the turnscrew – if you don't, an accident could happen and a nasty mark appear on your gun as a result. But please note that this pin is the only one with a slot that does not fit centrally flush when in position – so don't force it.

99.   Turning the gun upside down again, resting the face of the action on the edge of the bench, fully tighten up the trigger plate pin and then the hand pin. Take the trigger guard in the right hand, position it on the trigger plate and gently screw in a clockwise direction.

100.   Replace the trigger guard pin – again screw gently.

101.   Prior to replacing the bottom plate gently smear a thin film of grease or Vaseline on the mechanism of the action.

97

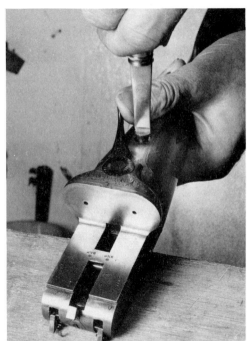

98

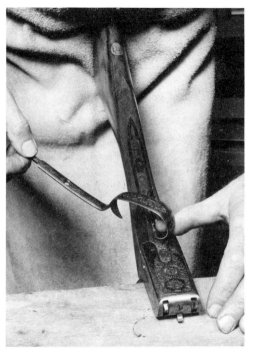

99

100

101

102, 103. Place the trigger plate in position. You should now have one pin left in the box! This is the bottom plate pin which should now be replaced. Screw fully home. Breathe a sigh of relief!

104. This would be an appropriate moment to look at the fore-end. The metalwork (called 'the iron') is removed from the wood by releasing two pins. The push rod is also secured by a further two pins. Firstly remove the one at its base, thus releasing the rod and revealing a second pin which holds the rod's 'tube' housing in position. Having removed all of these check for dirt, wear or damage, cleaning with a feather.

102

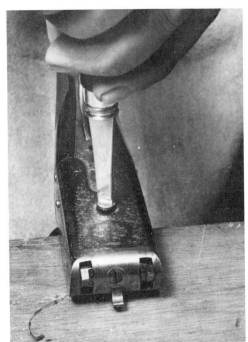

103

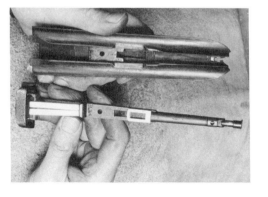

104

105, 106.   Put the gun back together, securing the barrels to the action, together with the fore-end. Insert your snap caps and now you can put your handiwork to the test.

107.   Close the gun, pull the triggers, open and . . . your snap caps should fly across the room. A smile will simultaneously appear across your face. But wait – try it once more for luck!

105

106

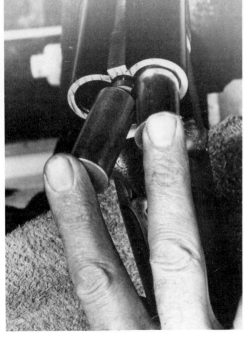

107

CHAPTER FIVE

The Sidelock

The sidelock shotgun is a much more difficult proposition than the boxlock. There are radical differences in its action design and construction and greater intricacies in its lock mechanism. Consequently there is a wider range of parts involved.

But the principle of the operation is basically the same. You take each stage as it comes, using the proper tools and the correct procedure. The only additional tool to those used on the boxlock is the main-spring clamp. Take plenty of time and be sure to double check on each move before using the turnscrew.

As a model for instruction I have chosen a Purdey sidelock ejector. It is hardly likely that if you are fortunate enough to own a Purdey you will take it into your own workshop and start stripping it down!

But my reason for choosing this particular gun is simple – as one of the, if not the, very best sidelocks to be found anywhere in the world it presents itself as the ideal illustration piece. The mechanism of a sidelock varies little in operation from the bottom grade to the top – what differs quite drastically is the standard of workmanship and materials.

As with the boxlock, stripping the sidelock will enable you to check for any wear or slight damage to the internal parts that would not have otherwise revealed itself until substantially worsened. If you do find anything amiss don't hesitate to take the gun to your local gunshop – repairs are a job for a trained gunmaker.

This should not be a cause for feeling dejected. You can be pleased you found whatever might be wrong with your gun and you may well have saved yourself both expense and inconvenience or even prevented an accident!

Whether after reading this step-by-step guide you intend to strip your gun or not, you should remember that in any event it really should be stripped and cleaned about every two years. This is important for both your safety and also for the gun's long life. If you look after it properly, it will in turn look after you! A well-cared-for gun is likely to maintain its price and give you good service.

1. Start at the beginning – remove the fore-end and barrels.
Close examination of the barrels is an obvious but very necessary part of the process. Check whether there are any signs of the ribs becoming loose. Sound barrels, with top and bottom ribs secure,

will normally ring clearly like a bell when suspended by the hook in the forward lump and tapped smartly. Barrels with loose ribs or with internal corrosion have a dull ring. Look carefully *into*, rather than through, the bores for signs of dents, usually found near the muzzles, bruises or pitting. If you do find anything wrong then the barrels should be taken to a competent gunmaker who can carry out the work necessary to put them right.

2.   I tend to deal with the barrels as a single item. So while with the action I will simply check each part as I strip it down, and then clean as I go through the stages of re-assembly, with the barrels I both check and clean them at the same time. This is purely because there are only a few parts involved and I feel it is wiser to complete this task before looking at the action. So my next step is to remove the extractor retaining pin – the process is identical to the boxlock, i.e. hold securely on the workbench with the left hand, with the lumps uppermost, and unscrew (placing the weight of your body with your shoulder directly above the turnscrew).

Remember that the fit of your turnscrew to the head of the screws should always be as near perfect as possible (preferably slightly smaller): if the turnscrew slips you can easily score metal or wood.

3.   Place the pin in the stripping box and then remove the extractor (ejector legs). You may find it best to hold the barrels between your legs against the bench so that both hands are free to lift the extractors out.

Put the extractors on one side and clean out the hole between the lumps and the small guide hole with a feather (as with the boxlock), wipe the lumps of the barrels clean and, above all, remove any dirt or grit that may have collected in the bites or the hook. Clean the extractor bed and finally the recesses for the cartridge rims in the chambers.

Examine the extractors for fractures or cracks, carefully wipe them clean, apply a smear of grease (or Vaseline) to both halves and put them together and place them back in their hole. Finally the retaining pin is cleaned and replaced.

Fit your cleaning rod jag or loop with a clean patch and remove any fouling from the inside of the barrels. Before putting the barrels back into the case apply a thin film of oil both inside and outside.

The final operation is to examine the fore-end, so when this is done place it safely aside to prevent any damage. We can now turn our full attention to the action.

1

2

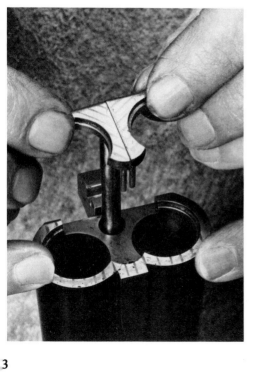

3

4 & 5.   The first step is to remove the trigger guard as we did with the boxlock. Making sure the gun is held secure against the bench by your left hand, you can now release the two pins (wood screws). The trigger guard itself is then normally removed by unscrewing in an anti-clockwise direction. The pins and trigger guard should of course go safely into the stripping box.

6.   The next step is to remove the sidelocks; this is done by unscrewing the pin (there is one on either side of the lock plate) shown in the photograph.

7.   It doesn't matter which lock comes out first, the right or the left. The inset picture in fact shows the left lock being removed after the right one has already been detached (featured in the other photograph).

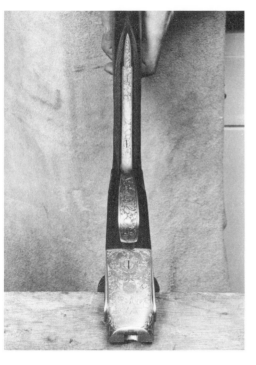

4

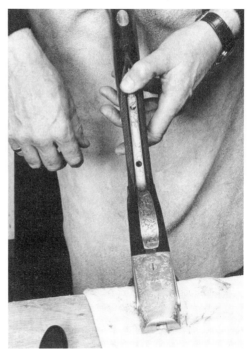

5

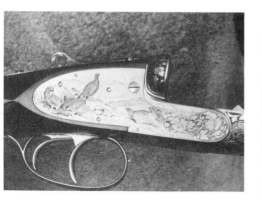

6

7

8.   Having removed the lock-plate pins, support the stock in the right hand. Gently (and make sure it is gently) tap the action on the bench. This should cause the lock plate to come free from the recess in the stock and drop into your left hand.

9.   This photograph shows how the plate fits into the stock and action. Note that the lock is in the cocked position.

10.   The first step in taking the action off the stock is to slacken the hand-pin and trigger plate pin – but do not remove either at this stage.

11.   Turning the gun the correct way up and supporting firmly on the bench, open the lever to its full extent with your left thumb and select the correct turnscrew to remove the breech pin. It is absolutely vital that you place the full weight of your body over the turnscrew as this should be the tightest pin in the gun. Needless to say a slip now could make a nasty, and very obvious, mark.

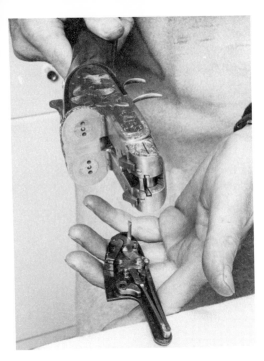

8

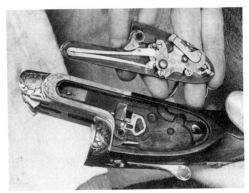

9

10

11

12.   Now withdraw the breech pin with the finger and thumb of the right hand.

13.   Turn the gun over and unscrew and remove the trigger plate pin and the hand pin.

14.   The trigger plate can now be lifted out of the stock.

15.   The action is now removed from the stock by supporting it in your right hand and – with the stock held close to your body with your left – gently push down with your right hand to ease the action away from the stock. Care must be taken not to damage the wood, especially the 'horns' on the stock. At no time must force be used! (See 16.)

12

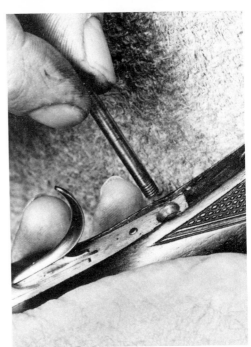

13

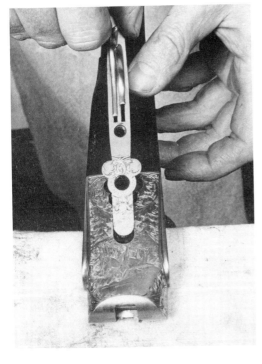

14

15

16

17.   With the innards of your gun revealed you can see for yourself how the safety mechanism works.

18 & 19.   The next step is to remove the easy or 'assisted' opening mechanism which is often found on Purdey and other good-quality sidelock guns. Lift out the two cams (they are simply close-fitted around a cross-pin) which will be marked R and L, denoting right and left.

17

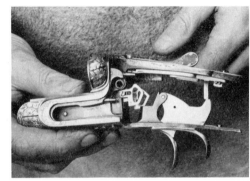

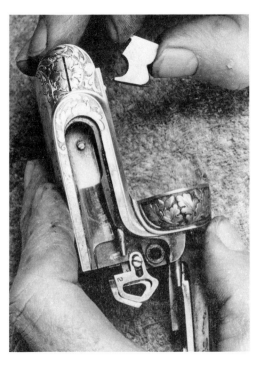

18

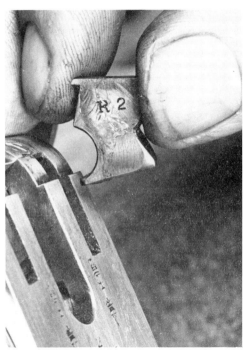

19

75

20.   Now remove the two rods which fit tightly behind the cams – they simply slide out. These are also marked, front left and front right.

21 & 22.   The cocking rods should then be detached from the action by removing the securing pin on each rod.

23.   The cocking rods must be withdrawn gently – they are long and slender and could easily be damaged.

24.   The next job is to remove the top lever spring.

20

21

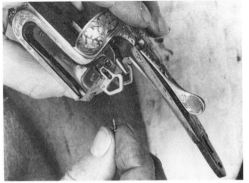

22

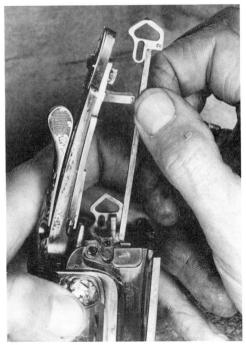

23

24

25.   Holding the action in the left hand, push the lever fully open thus compressing the spring. Holding the spring clamp in your right hand, place the slot in the clamp over the spring and gently release the top lever. The spring will now hold itself securely in the clamp. Unscrew the lever spring pin and remove, still holding the clamp in position. Some top lever springs have only an integral lug on the spring which pulls out when the spring is freed of pressure. The pin having been removed, the lever spring itself can now be taken out of the underside of the strap of the action by lifting while still held in the clamp. To remove the spring safely from the clamp place it and the clamp in a piece of rag in your left hand. Compress the spring with your left hand and withdraw the clamp with your right. The rag will prevent the spring from jumping into the air and you can gently allow the spring to open to its widest.

26 & 27.   The next task is to detach the safety mechanism. Hold the action upside down in your left hand in order to remove the 'sugar tong' spring. Simply unscrew the pin (as shown in the photograph).

25

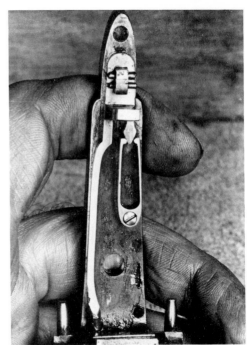

26

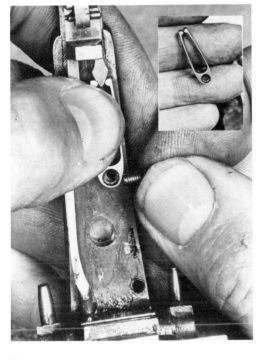

27

28 & 29.   Hold the action on its side so that the strap lays on a cloth on the bench. Push the thumbpiece retaining pins out with the side of a turnscrew.

30.   The pins can now be withdrawn with the finger and thumb. You will find that these are normally marked 1 and 2 to avoid confusion when replaced.

31.   You should now be able to push out the thumbpiece, thus allowing the safety slide to be removed from the underside of the strap of the action. It is worth noting if any dirt and grit has accumulated on the underside of the strap and in the working parts.

28

29

30

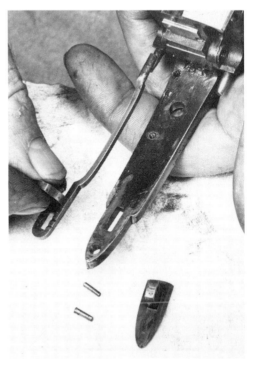

31

32.   Removing the lever work. Place the action flat on the bench, holding the lever in the closed position. Select the proper turnscrew and proceed to unscrew and remove the lever pin.

33 & 34.   To remove the top lever itself we have first to detach it from its securing spindle. This is done by gently tapping a pin punch into the top of the lever (where the screw was removed). But be careful to choose a punch which fits correctly as it is all too easy to damage the thread inside the spindle. Hold the action in your left hand ensuring that the lever is in the closed position, insert the punch into the hole and tap gently. The spindle will start to come away at the bottom of the action.

35.   The top lever will now lift out of the top of the action.

32

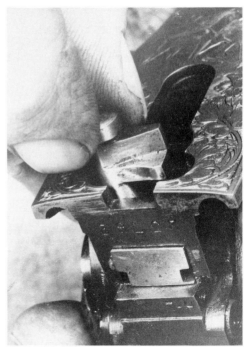

33

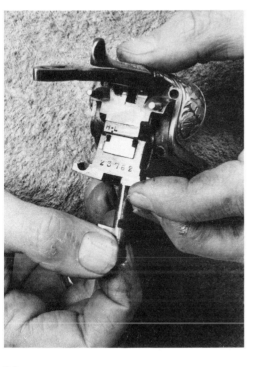

34

35

36.   The bolt is now removed by withdrawing with the finger and thumb of your right hand.

37.   This photograph shows the fitting together of the lever, spindle and bolt.

38.   Now turn your attention to the trigger plate. The first pin to be removed is the top pin in the photograph, which holds the trigger return spring. This is made from thin spring steel which is split to serve both triggers. It prevents the triggers from rattling and presses them down through the trigger slots in the plate.

39 & 40.   Gently lift out the spring, by turning and lifting it at the same time so as to unhook the two prongs at its base.

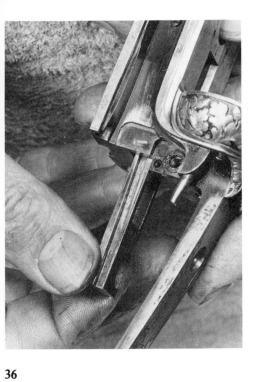

36

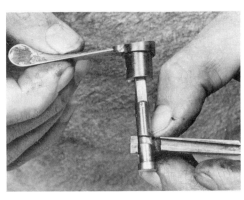

37

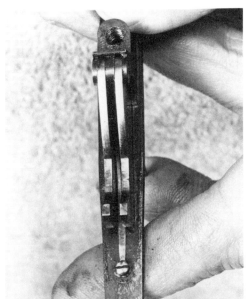

38

39

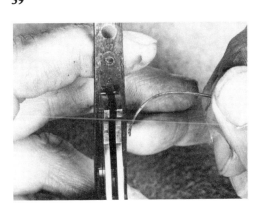

40

41.   The trigger return spring with the pin in position – note the dirt which has accumulated.

42.   Holding the trigger plate in your left hand, the next operation is to remove the pin on which both triggers pivot.

43 & 44.   These photographs show the pin being unscrewed and withdrawn.

45 & 46.   It is now a simple operation to withdraw the triggers from the plate.

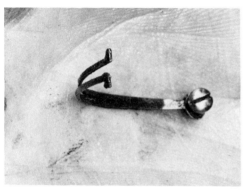

41

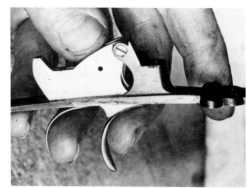

42

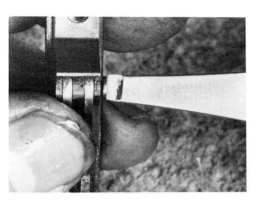

43

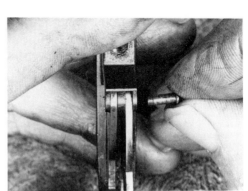

44

45

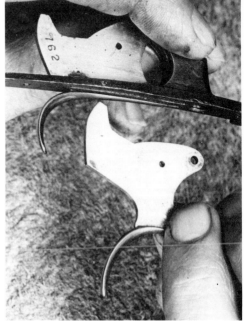

47.   We are now left with the trigger plate showing the two slots, one for each trigger blade, and, as can be seen, unless the triggers are removed the mechanism just cannot be cleaned properly.

48.   Your box of parts should now look something like this. Now examine the part of the gun's mechanism which makes the sidelock shotgun so different from the boxlock and is also largely the reason for sidelocks usually being more expensive.

The sidelock derives its name from the fact that the sideplates, which look so attractive on the gun, carry the more vital parts of the firing mechanism. Their making is an intricate skill and reflects the work of an accomplished gunsmith.

Because of the complexity of the mechanism it is wiser to have a separate box in which you place each part of the sidelocks as you dismantle them. This will make re-assembly much simpler.

49.   Before starting this job it will be worthwhile studying one of the lockplates to see how the mechanism operates. Pressure on the trigger lifts the sear arm, the sear nose therefore comes away from the bent of the tumbler thus releasing the main spring. This propels the hammer forward to strike the detonator in the base of the cartridge. On no account be tempted to satisfy your curiosity by lifting the sear. You could damage both the mechanism and yourself (the main spring could fly out and break or give you a very nasty blow).

50.   Under no circumstances should the sidelocks be dismantled unless you have a proper mainspring clamp – this is the only additional piece of equipment to that needed to dismantle a boxlock action.

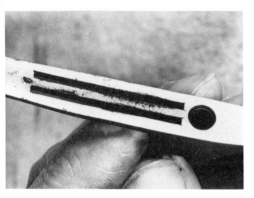

47

48

49

50

51.   The first step is to remove the cam – the number 2 on the gun in the picture merely indicates that this is the second gun of a pair of guns numbered 1 and 2.

52.   Taking the spring clamp in the right hand place the jaws over the spring (as illustrated in the photograph) and gently tighten. This will compress and give you control of the main spring.

53.   Having clamped the main spring unhook it from the swivel link which joins the spring to the bottom of the hammer. This will allow you to detach the main spring from the spring clamp by placing a cloth around it and gently unscrewing the clamp. The power in a main spring is considerable so don't attempt to release the clamp without first covering with a cloth.

54.   We now remove the spring which keeps tension on the intercepting sear. This sear is a secondary safety device which will check the hammer if it is accidentally jarred out of position in the bent whilst the safety catch is on. Unscrew the pin which secures the spring, but do not remove the pin entirely. The spring will be retained in position by a small protrusion slotting into a groove cut in the lock plate. The spring also retains itself by compression, the end of it lodging against the intercepting sear.

55.   To remove the spring completely from the lock plate, gently ease it away from the intercepting sear by placing a turnscrew underneath the spring and twist to lift the spring upwards. Place the spring in the box.

51

52

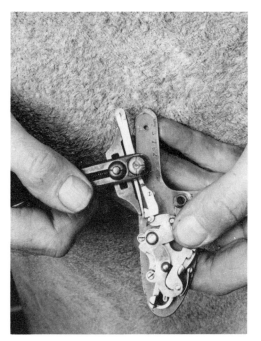

53

54

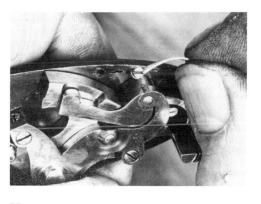

55

56.   The attention is now turned to the bridle. First remove the locking pin. While a Purdey gun will usually have a locking pin, you may find that many other guns of similar construction don't.

57.   Remove the pin completely.

58.   You can now slacken the three pins indicated (see the photograph).

59 & 60.   With the aid of your turnscrew, gently ease the bridle away from the lock plate until you are able to lift it completely clear of the hammer, sear and intercepting sear (see photograph 62). If by chance one of the three pins falls away from the bridle you will find that there will be an indication mark on each to ensure its return to the correct slot. You can now also lift out the intercepting sear.

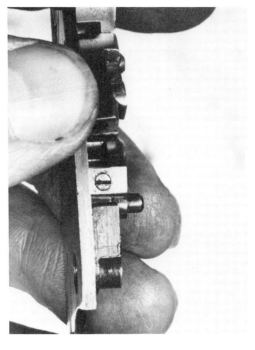

56

57

58

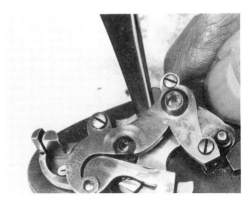

59

60

61.   You are now left with the hammer, sear and sear spring.

62 & 63.   Compress the sear spring (as shown), holding it in position, and remove the hammer with the left hand.

64.   Ease the sear down gently and remove it.

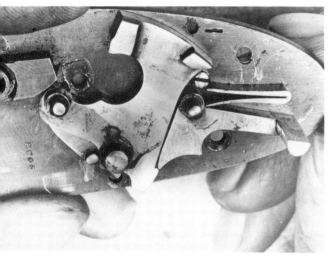

61

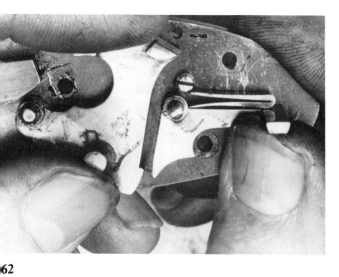

62

63

64

95

65.   Finally the spring is taken out by releasing the pin. The spring should be eased away from the plate with the end of a turnscrew.

66.   This photograph shows all the component parts of the sidelock. Congratulations! You are half-way there; you have completely stripped your gun. During the stages of dismantling you will have been carrying out a visual inspection for dirt, wear or damage. So remember if you spotted any sign of a fault during the process you should now take it to your gunsmith. But, hopefully, the gun will only need cleaning. Now, as you re-assemble, is the time to check and clean each part.

The first part to receive attention will be the action. Thoroughly clean the slots in the action body. A piece of clean cloth placed over the nose of a narrow file will enable you to wipe internal areas free of dirt. Small holes and slots should be probed with the aid of a feather. Having made sure the action is clean commence the first stage of re-assembly. All parts should be given a thin application of oil or white Vaseline but be careful not to apply too much to any part as this may result in dirt being attracted. The golden rule is wipe on and wipe off.

67.   The first stage in the re-assembly of the gun is the lever work. Making sure that the bolt is clean, lightly lubricate and replace in its recess in the action also making sure that the bolt is pressed fully home.

68.   Having made sure that the lever spindle and its hole are clean, replace in the action.

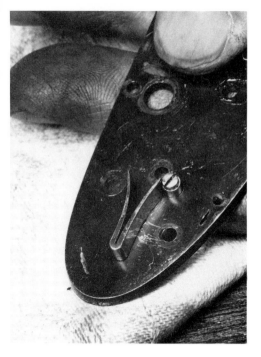

65

66

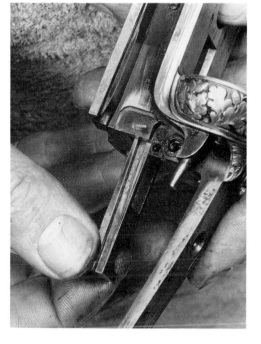

67

68

69.   Holding the lever in position with your left hand (firmly against the stomach) insert the end of the spindle into the spindle hole with your right hand.

70.   Push the spindle home as far as you can.

71.   Select a pin punch which is smaller in diameter than the head of the spindle and secure the punch in the vice (as shown in photograph). Placing the head of the spindle directly on the pin punch, take a wooden mallet or hide hammer and gently tap the head of the lever until the lever sits flush on the top strap.

72.   From the box of parts select the lever pin (the one with a sloping head). Screw into the spindle with finger and thumb as far as possible.

69

70

71

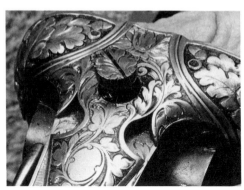

72

73.   Place the base of the action on the bench top. Hold the lever in the 'home' position, select your turnscrew (not forgetting that the blade needs to be just fractionally smaller than the width of the slot in the pin) and start to tighten in the correct manner by placing the weight of your body and shoulder directly above the pin.

74.   The pin should now be in the central position with the head flush and the slot pointing up the barrels.

75.   Making sure that the vice guards are in position, take the lever spring from the stripping box and place between the jaws of the vice and gently compress the spring. Care needs to be taken as only the extreme ends of both legs are compressed. Should you compress from the 'V' end of the spring you risk cracking the spring or weakening its power. Now slide the spring clamp (the piece of metal with the slot cut out of it) over the spring thus holding it in the compressed position. Release the vice and the lever spring is firmly held by the clamp.

76.   With the lever spring held in the clamp replace it in the action and, with your right hand, screw the pin into the hole shown, and fully tighten. Now push the top lever open to the fullest extent of its travel which will compress the lever spring and so allow you to remove the spring clamp.

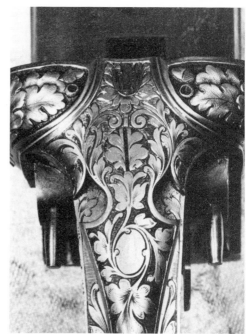

73

74

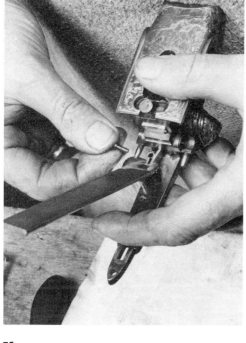

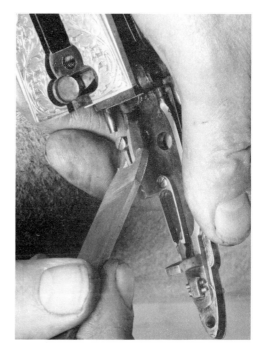

75

76

77.   Take the two cocking limbs from the stripping box. Make sure that the two slots in the action body have been thoroughly cleaned with the use of a feather. Taking the right-hand limb, wipe with grease before inserting into the slot in the action. Take care not to force or bend the arm.

78.   Select the correct pin and screw in. Note the dirt on this part in the photograph – it was taken during the stripping-down process!

Don't forget that the left-hand side is normally marked by the means of a shallow groove in the end of the pin. Remove the turnscrew and test with finger and thumb that the limb works freely. The same operation is repeated for the right-hand side.

We can now begin to re-assemble the safety work. This consists of the safety slide, the thumb piece, the two pegs which hold the thumb piece on the slide and the 'sugar tong' spring.

Holding the action in the left hand, turn it upside down. Lay the safety slide on the inside of the top strap, with the leg of the slide fitting into the hole that is clearly visible. This reverses the procedure shown in photograph 31.

79.   Now slot the thumb piece back into the top strap from above and push in the two securing pegs marked 1 and 2 – number 1 should go nearest the breech end.

80.   Push firmly home so that the ends of the pins lie flush with the edges of the safety slide.

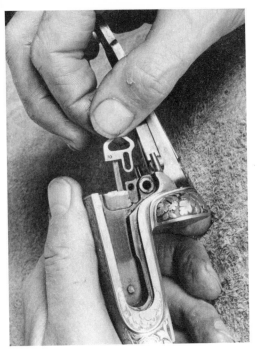

77

78

79

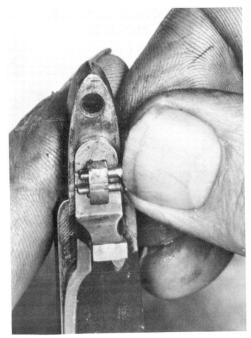

80

81.   The final operation in replacing the safety catch is to lay the 'sugar tong' spring on the underside of the strap (as shown) and screw in the retaining pin.

82.   The next operation is to replace the cams marked 'right' and 'left'. They simply enter the slots which have been machined in the action body.

83.   The two round pieces of steel (the rods which left the cams) are also marked right and left. They simply push into the holes provided for them at the rear end of the action. Hold by the tapered end when inserting.

84.   Place the action to one side, as attention is now needed in the re-assembly of the triggers into the trigger plate. Make sure that both the blades of the triggers, and their slots in the trigger plate, are quite clean. Holding the trigger plate in your left hand, with the rounded end pointed away from you, place the larger of the two triggers into the slot on the right-hand side. This is the rear trigger which normally fires the left-hand barrel. Now slot in the front trigger, which fires the right-hand barrel.

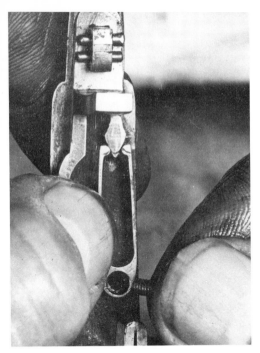

81

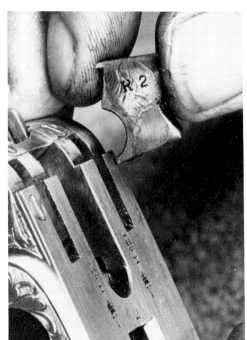

82

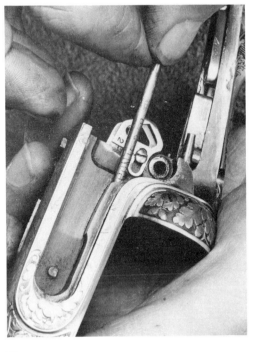

83

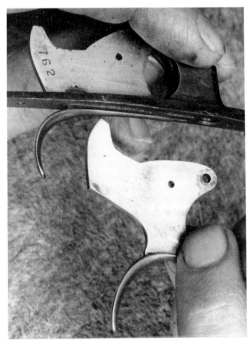

84

85.   Turn the trigger plate upside down. Support the triggers with the fingers of the left hand and align the pivot holes and the pillar and carefully insert the pin through the three holes.

86.   Finally, carefully screw the pin home.

87.   Take the trigger return spring (photograph 43) and insert the two legs between the blades of the triggers. A small hole will be noted in each blade. These are to accommodate the legs on the end of the split spring. Twist the spring gently sideways and each of the legs should pop into its fixing hole.

88.   Lay the spring flat and secure it to the trigger plate by screwing in the pin.

We are now able to refit the stock to the action; but before doing so, examine the 'head' of the stock for any signs of cracks or splits or seepage of oil into the grain. If even slight splits or cracks are detected, then it would obviously be wise to seek the advice of your local gunsmith about trying to prevent the flaws splitting any further. If you discover an excess amount of oil endeavour to wipe as dry as possible and test with a thumb nail to see if any softening of the wood has occurred. Never try to dry out excessively oiled wood with heat as this will invariably cause the grain to separate and ultimately fracture.

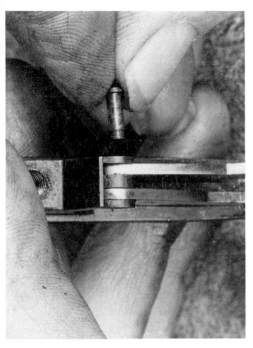

85

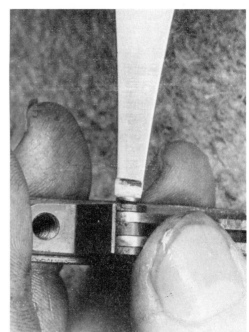

86

87

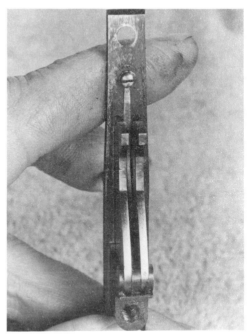

88

89.   We earlier stressed the importance of taking the utmost care
when removing the action from the stock – the same applies when
replacing it. It is all too easy to spoil the fit if you try to force the
parts together. Supporting the stock in the left hand and close to
the body, take the action in the right hand, making sure that the
safety mechanism is on safe. Gently ease the action onto the head of
the stock.

90.   The wood at the head of the stock should not necessarily be
'flush' or exactly level with the sides of the action. Turn the action
and stock upside down, taking care meanwhile to hold the two
together and place the face of the action on the edge of the bench
(as shown). Supporting the end of the stock with your stomach,
while at the same time gently pressing inwards, you will have both
hands free to pick up the assembled trigger plate and insert it into
its recess in the bottom of the action.

91.   You can now insert and tighten the trigger plate pin and the
'hand' pin.

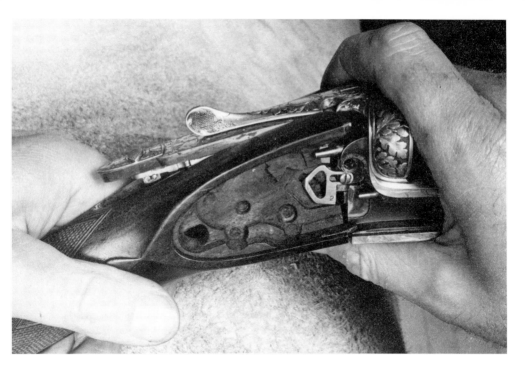

89

90

91

92 & 93.   Turn the action the correct way up ready to replace the breech pin. Screw the pin in as far as possible with the finger and thumb, making sure of course that you keep the top lever in the 'open' position. Supporting the bottom of the action on the bench, with the top lever open, start to tighten the breech pin with your turnscrew. The breech pin has a sloping top to the head which, when fully home, lies completely flush.

94.   Turn the gun upside down, once again resting the flats of the action against the bench and, supporting the end of the stock against the body, we can now refit the trigger guard. Make sure its thread is clean and commence to screw, in a clockwise direction, until the trigger guard is screwed fully home. The final operation is to press the tang of the guard gently into its recess and carefully screw in the two trigger guard pins. These will be seen to be like ordinary wood screws (in some respects) but with engraved heads which are shaped to fit into the rounded surface of the trigger guard tang. For a neater and more professional-looking job try to have the screws tight but with the slots pointing centrally down the length of the gun. But do not be tempted to overtighten as this may damage the thread!

95.   Put the stock aside so that you can begin to re-assemble the locks. In this case we are showing the re-assembly of the right-hand lock but it matters little which one you choose to re-assemble first.

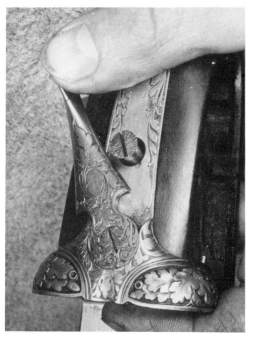

92

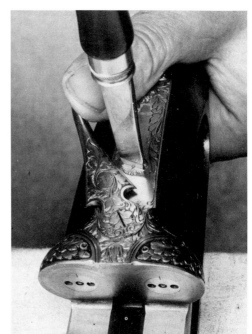

93

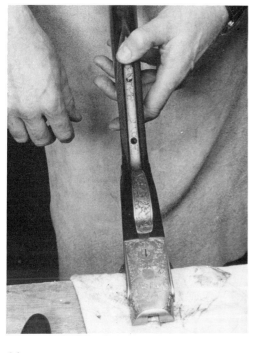

94

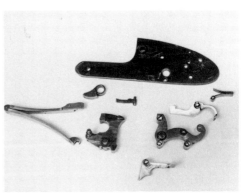

95

96.   Make sure that all the holes in the lockplate are clean by again using a feather. Wipe the plate with a piece of clean cloth and you are now ready to replace the sear spring having also smeared it lightly with Vaseline. This is simply refixed in position with the screw shown. The sear is next – note that the sear spring must be compressed by the sear to enable the hammer to be held in the proper position.

97.   Replace the hammer by simply slotting it into place. Take the pressure off the sear and it will immediately hold the hammer.

98.   The intercepting sear and bridle are assembled (they are shaped to fit together naturally) and, holding the plate in your left hand, put the two parts directly over the hammer with the two holes lining up on the two studs and gently press them down into position with your fingers. This is a reasonably straightforward reverse of the process of stripping the lock down.

99.   Finally screw the three pins home, again making sure you have selected the correct turnscrew.

100.   Replace the locking pin at the top of the bridle.

101.   Taking the plate in your left hand use your right to replace the small spring so that the small protrusion along its middle fits into the slot in the plate. Now tighten its securing screw.

96

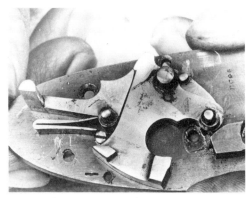

97

98

99

100

101

102. The penultimate operation is the replacement of the main spring. Great care must be taken, otherwise an accident can easily occur for, if the main spring is suddenly released and is unrestrained, it could possibly fracture in two halves. Having a new main spring made can be a costly business and your gun could be out of use for weeks. Secure the main spring clamp in the vice, exactly as shown, and, gently turning the screw of the clamp, the spring will start to compress. Do not forget to support the spring with the thumb and forefinger of your left hand. Screw the clamp home as far as possible.

103. First hook the end of the spring around the little peg on the cam. Gently push the clamp, in turn moving the cam slightly forward, thus allowing the peg of the spring to sit in the hole shown. Gently release the clamp having moved the left hand back to support both the main spring and the plate. This will prevent the spring jumping out – the spring itself is under considerable pressure so be especially careful.

104. The final operation in the replacement of the lock is the fitting of the small cam marked 2 (this number merely indicates that the gun is the number two of a pair). Then lightly grease the mechanism. The same method of re-assembly applies to the left-hand lock.

105. The complete lock is now ready to be returned to its recess in the stock.

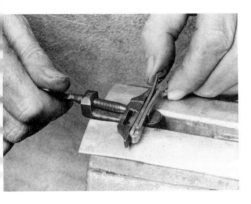

102

103

104

105

106.   Locate the small projection (lip) at the front of the lock plate into the corresponding slot in the action recess, and the plate should press snugly into place.

107.   Replace the lock plate pin, not forgetting that the left-hand side is usually marked with a small identifying groove on the end of the pin. Turn the gun over onto the other side, and similarly replace the left-hand lock.

108.   The lock plates must not be forced into place – they have been made to fit perfectly and thus minimise the entry of dust and the gun's arch-enemy, moisture!

Your job is now complete. You can now put the barrels, stock and fore-end back together, drop two snap caps into the chambers and pull the triggers. Open the gun, watch the two snap caps eject . . . and feel proud of yourself!

106

107

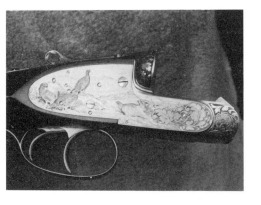

108

CHAPTER SIX

The Over-and-Under

More and more shooters are now using the over-and-under shotgun, particularly the ever-growing band of clay pigeon enthusiasts. These guns are imported from all corners of the world. Italy, Spain, Belgium, Russia, the USA, Czechoslovakia and Japan are among the many suppliers to the British gun trade.

Because of the wide sources of origin the design and specification of these guns vary considerably. You would need to carry an extremely wide range of tools to enable you to strip down all the models which are on the market.

Here we will simply look at how you can help maintain your gun in top condition so that it functions properly, is safe and maintains its value.

The gun chosen as an example is a Nikko trap gun, made in Japan. This firm ceased to manufacture guns some time ago.

Although the Miroku is also made in Japan it nonetheless has completely different ejectors to the Nikko – which illustrates the diversity of guns around today. One of the most reliable guns of all, the Beretta, is different again.

We will remove the stock (one of the parts which varies little) and the action in order to examine and clean the mechanism and also take out the extractors/ejectors. This is a straightforward process and only basic tools are needed. It will prove beneficial in terms of proper maintenance and will also give the shooter a greater insight into how his gun works.

In common with the boxlock and sidelock guns examined earlier the stripping-down operation will also reveal any faults or parts of the mechanism which need attention.

1. Having removed the barrels from the action you will note that the extractors are standing proud of the breech face of the barrels. Before the extractor can be removed, we must compress the coil spring which pushes out the extractor. This is done by holding the barrels in the left hand and pushing the face of the barrels up against the front of your bench, thus compressing the spring (as shown).

2. Having selected a small pin punch, with the right hand carefully remove the small cam roller.

3. Gently release the pressure of the barrels until the spring is extended. You will now be able to draw out one of the extractors.

4. The spring and a small peg are now revealed.

1

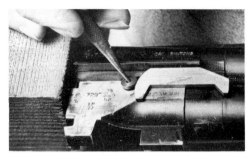

2

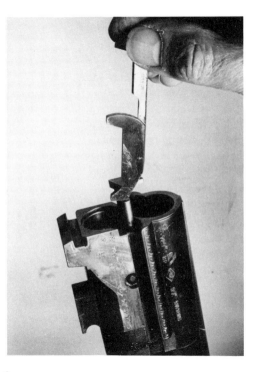

3

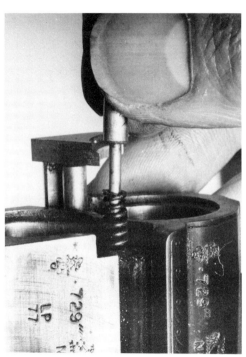

4

5.   Remove the peg and the spring can then be withdrawn. Repeat the operation on the other side.

6.   Put the barrels in a safe place and examine the extractors for any sign of wear or cracks. Remember to place the parts you have dismantled into a stripping box.

7.   Now clean out the holes which accommodate the spring and also make sure that the machine slots on either side of the barrels are perfectly clean. It is surprising how much dirt adheres to these surfaces.

Having checked and cleaned the extractors grease lightly, but make sure that *both* springs are cleaned (a little grease on these will do no harm!). Replace the springs, then the pegs, and slide the extractor into the machine slot until the bottom of the extractor comes to rest on the head of the peg.

You must now compress the coil spring in the same manner as in the first stages of stripping. Replace the small cam roller, and gently release the pressure and the extractor is secured. This operation is repeated on the other side. Finally wipe over the lumps (steels) i.e. the parts of the barrel which are normally concealed when the gun is closed. Make sure that both the hook (which accommodates the cross-pin) and the bite (that houses the draw bolt) are perfectly clean.

It goes without saying that the insides of the barrels should be spotless – this will of course include the chamber rims which should always be kept clean. A build-up of residues in the rims can cause cartridges to stick and the gun to jam shut. The gun may also fire prematurely on closing.

8.   Removal of the stock from the action. On this particular model a rubber recoil pad is fitted which is fixed by two Philips-type screws. Ordinary slot-headed screws can also be encountered. It is essential that you use only the proper type of screwdriver to remove them. You will see from the photograph that the heads of the screws are not visible. A small slit in the pad shows where they were originally inserted.

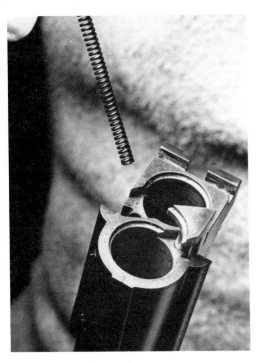

5

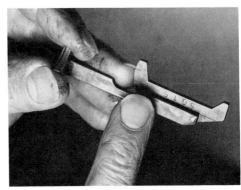

6

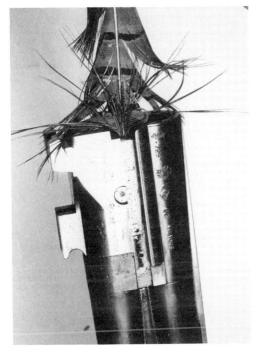

7

8

9.   Take care when inserting the screwdriver through the rubber that the 'cross' or blade of the screwdriver lines up with the cross or slot in the head of the screw. This will of course be immediately beneath the slit in the pad. Holding the stock in the left hand, and pressed close to the body, undo each screw until the wood and the pad separate. Take care since the pad is sometimes also glued to the butt.

10.   The pin (wood screw) which secures the trigger guard *must* be removed *before* the stock bolt is unscrewed (otherwise the tang or tail of the guard may be bent as it takes the weight of the stock when it comes loose). Make sure, of course, that you have selected a turnscrew which fits properly, otherwise you may damage the head of the screw. This is best removed by placing the face of the action against the edge of the workbench, supporting the end of the stock against the stomach and bringing the right shoulder directly over the turnscrew. This is the method which is adopted in the removal of all pins (screws).

11.   There are two methods of removing the long stock bolt which goes through the length of the stock and screws into the back of the action and which usually has a normal slotted head. One means is by the use of a 'ratchet' screwdriver providing of course that the hole is wide enough to admit the ratchet portion. Otherwise a long turnscrew will be needed with a blade measuring approximately $1/2''$ wide. Hold the stock close to the body and grip firmly with the left hand. Place the end of the turnscrew in the hole and gently feed it in so that the bolt at the bottom of the hole is felt with the end of the turnscrew. Rotate the turnscrew and you should be able to feel it slip into the slot in the bolt head. Having done this, grip the turnscrew tightly and begin to unscrew in an anti-clockwise direction. It may need quite a lot of force to release the stock bolt since it obviously needs to be absolutely dead tight. Unscrew and, holding the action and stock together, turn the stock upside down and the stock bolt should drop out.

12.   Separate the action from the stock by holding the action in the left hand and the stock in the right. Tap the action on the bench and the stock should loosen and start to come away.

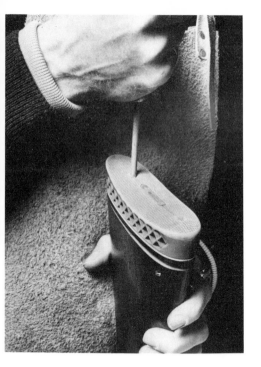

9

10

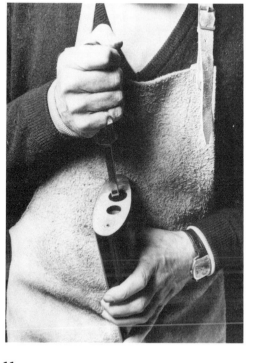

11

12

13.   Finally the two will part. Place the action aside and examine the stock closely, especially where it has been recessed to house the mechanism. This necessary hollowing weakens the stock at that point so examine carefully for any splitting which, if found, *must* be attended to at once.

14.   Place the stock carefully aside and examine the action. The trigger guard on this model is removed by giving it half a turn and lifting upwards; other types of gun may have a guard which has to be rotated against a screw thread.

15.   Now we can see the mechanism. Look for dirt and any visible signs of wear. Wipe clean and lubricate sparingly.

16.   If you should wish to remove a striker (or firing pin) select a pin punch and gently tap out the retaining pin (see the photograph). This will allow the striker to be withdrawn from the back of the action.

17.   Having ensured that the gun is clean and free of defects now put the stock back onto the action. Great care must be taken in this operation to avoid damage to the 'horns' of the stock. These enable the head of the stock to fit snugly into the action and prevent any sideways movement. Any damage at this point could spoil that fit. Replace the stock bolt and fully tighten. This pulls the action and stock tightly together so ensures that the vibration of firing does not cause the bolt to work loose. The final operation is to replace the recoil pad, taking great care to ensure that the screws are located properly and that the pad edges are flush with the stock.

If during the examination you have found anything slightly or seriously wrong, i.e. wear on the metal parts or a small crack in the head of the stock, take the gun to a competent gunsmith for examination and repair. It is not advisable to attempt to undertake extensive repairs yourself – stick to cleaning and checking.

13

14

15

16

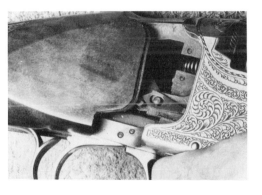

17

CHAPTER SEVEN

Stock Renovation

The woodwork of a gun, i.e. the stock and fore-end, are the most variable components of the gun since these parts are, at the outset, subject to the vagaries of density and grain found in the living tree. The exact grain structure, weight and figure of the stock vary between blanks cut from one tree and another. Even blanks cut from the same part of the tree can show remarkable differences and no two stocks are ever absolutely identical in every way.

Walnut is the wood which, over many centuries, has been found to embody the essential qualities required of a gun stock. These properties consist of ease of working and resistance to splitting, comparative lightness combined with strength and flexibility, since a stock flexes dramatically as the gun is fired thus absorbing much recoil. Finally the grain structure of walnut adds a bonus in the subtle nuances of colour it imparts to the appearance of a gun stock.

In some ways a stock is like a damascus barrel in that the harder age rings accept colour less readily than the pith wood between them, thus creating the light and dark shades of colour so familiar in a gunstock.

The best gun stock walnut comes from France where the climate seems, for some intangible reason, to produce ideal conditions in which to grow good walnut. In fact much French walnut finds its way into the far more lucrative, and exacting, furniture veneer industry. But in several other parts of the world, wherever the walnut tree grows well, gun stock wood can be found. These parts include North America, Italy and even Persia (now Iran).

As a generality wood producing the best 'figure' (swirls in the grain structure) occurs at the base of the tree and is commonly called 'root walnut' but from higher up the tree, where the grain straightens out with the trunk, comes the greater proportion of walnut found on less than 'best' gunstocks. The least attractive of these cheaper stock blanks are known in the trade as 'Greys'. The age and diameter of the tree also has an impact on the quality of the 'figure'. Stock blanks for pairs of guns are often chosen from the pairs of thicker forked branches. Sections of the trunk containing knots from smaller branches are normally discarded since these can impart splits or 'shakes' to a finished stock which may not become apparent till much work has been done.

Proper drying out and seasoning of a quality stock blank over a period of five to ten years is necessary gradually to relieve the wood of moisture and allow it to 'settle' before being selected for stocking a gun. (This period can be reduced on lesser quality wood.) Once properly seasoned the wood will not 'move' again or change its basic shape. But, conversely, wood which is still 'wet' (i.e. not properly seasoned) can change the stock's dimensions dramatically after fitting or even split, making all the stocker's work a waste of effort.

Kiln drying is a modern method of accelerating the drying-out process but this is generally used, with much success, on the straighter and less complex grained stocks of mass-produced and fairly inexpensive guns. However, the process is so advanced that some surprisingly expensive imported guns have kiln-dried wood. But if moisture is drawn too rapidly from the wood by the use of drying chambers the wood becomes porous and loses its close-grained density and much of its weight.

No other feature of a gun responds so well to the care and attention lavished upon it as the woodwork. Since English guns were, and are, built to last many lifetimes the amateur gunsmith owes a moral, as well as practical, responsibility to some future owner of his gun to take great care to achieve the best finish to the stock that he is capable of.

When considering removing a dent, bruise or scratch, it must be realised that the whole stock may have to be stripped of its surface finish and repolished. It is difficult, if not impossible, to refinish a small area of the stock without creating a patch of different colour or polish. This is due, at least in part, to age patination. Refinishing can be a lengthy and painstaking operation if you are hoping to achieve a really professional finish.

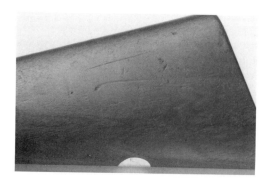

1.   Dark, featureless and full of dents – ready for restoration.

Before beginning work you must decide what type of finish is required – an 'English' oil finish, French (or button) polishing or using one of the ready made-up polishes that are on the market.

The most difficult finish to apply is, without doubt, an 'English' oil finish. However, this is particularly appropriate if the gun has a highly figured stock. To achieve a good finish and enhance the beauty of such a gun will need many hours spent in preparation even before any oil is applied.

One of the potential problems, when polishing gunstocks, is to allow the polishing medium to enter the chequering area. This must be avoided if possible, although inevitably a certain amount will clog the edge of the chequering pattern and can be removed later. Let us, therefore, consider some of the various polishes that are commonly in use.

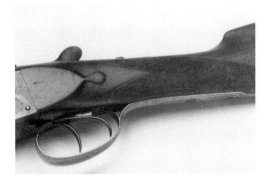

2. The chequering has become full of dirt and the drop points have lost their sharpness.

'English' oil finish

Properly done the most appealing of all gunstock finishes, but the most difficult to achieve to a 'professional' standard. The process is time consuming and laborious, both in the stock's preparation and in the correct application of the oil finisher. Normally a mixture of pure turpentine and raw linseed oil is used which should be applied with a pad made by folding a piece of clean cotton cloth; old-fashioned bedsheet flannel is ideal. To ensure a good surface the grain must first be raised before polishing. The grain can also be filled using any well-known proprietary brand of filler.

An important point to remember is that at no time must the oil be allowed to dry off when lying on the surface of the stock. Any surplus must be wiped off after each application using a piece of clean cotton cloth and rubbed over with the palm of your bare hand.

Finishing a stock by hand gives the wood a high degree of polish and protection from moisture and this is best achieved by laying on coat after coat of 'mixture' and rubbing off between coats. Doing this in a warm atmosphere, or slightly warming the mixture, is preferable. This method may take several weeks to complete, applying a coat of oil every day. So, unless you have both the patience and a highly-figured walnut stock, which make the effort worth while, think very seriously before even starting.

French (or button) polish

An attractive and fairly durable method of finishing a stock although rather prone to surface wear and scratches. Many London and provincial gunmakers use this method as a final finish in stock presentation. French or button polish, with a mere touch of raw linseed oil (to help in spreading the polish), is evenly applied to the stock. When finished no smears should be visible and the stock has an even thickness of polish all over.

Practise on a piece of scrap wood a number of times before attempting work on your stock.

Proprietary brands

These preparations are normally supplied with step-by-step instructions which must be strictly followed if you are to achieve the results suggested by the manufacturers. Most have been tried and extensively tested by the makers and can be expected to give a durable and long-lasting finish.

Select your choice of polishing preparation with care, and read the instructions written on the box properly before making a choice. This can help make the difference between being highly satisfied with your handiwork or being extremely disappointed with your failure.

3. One of the brands that can be recommended.

Preparation of the stock

Certain basic tools are required – the list is as follows:

kitchen knife	alkanet root dye
engineer's vice and bench	other wood dyes
bench rest (or horse)	turpentine
clean rag (cotton)	linseed oil
vice guards	a selection of glass or sand papers
fine wire wool	

As before, place vice guards on the jaws of your vice to prevent the action body from being marked or damaged. If your gun has a fixed toe (which operates the extractors) protruding from the knuckle of the action, which is retained by a pin, then you should remove it temporarily. This will enable you to secure your action more firmly in the vice and avoid the risk of snapping off the toe.

If the toe is permanently fixed then take even greater care not to damage or break it when holding the action in the vice since such a repair could be very expensive.

It is also a good idea to detach the trigger guard and tape over the monogram oval to prevent scratching. Ideally both guard and oval would have been let further into the stock when the gun was made to avoid their standing proud of the surface. Other metalwork could be protected with masking tape.

Having secured the action in the vice, support the stock on its side by placing the bench rest directly beneath it so that when pressure is applied the stock will remain rigid.

The actual work of removing the old polish can now begin.

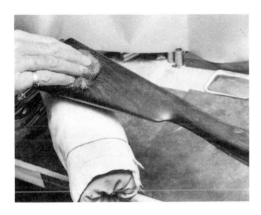

4.   Step One. A 'bench rest' for the stock – use some protection for the vice jaws.

If the stock has a thick layer of old finish, or an accumulation of grease and dirt, you will tackle it with wire wool. Switch to fine sand paper as you get closer to the wood. Some are tempted to use a scraper but I would suggest that you avoid this option as the stock could be easily damaged.

Having rubbed down the entire surface, when one side is properly completed, turn the stock over and repeat.

The next stage is to examine and, if necessary, remove any serious marks from the surface of the stock. These may include deep scratches, gouges, dents or cuts. The best method of removing these is the use of a round-ended kitchen knife of which the last inch or so is heated to red heat in a flame – a propane blowlamp is ideal. A thoroughly soaked cloth, or piece of newspaper folded into three thicknesses, is then placed immediately onto the mark and the hot knife point is pressed onto the paper until it begins to dry out. Take care not to leave the red-hot knife in place too long as the paper will quickly dry and burn, and secondly, the stock may also be scorched. Once the paper has released its moisture as steam and turned crisp repeat the process, using another part of the paper, as often as is needed to lift the dent. The idea is that the steam enters the grain of the wood at the mark and swells the grain thus closing the hole or cut from the inside.

The only alternative to 'swelling the grain' at the dent is to remove surrounding wood to the level of the bottom of the dent. This may create a flat on the stock's contour or, worse still, alter its shape. The other least satisfactory choice is to use hot melted shellac as a filler which in almost all circumstances will colour differently to the wood and show as a dark patch on the stock.

Once the most serious marks are dealt with, start to smooth the stock's surface. Selecting a medium grade of sand or glass paper (folded into a pad), move gradually over the entire stock surface evenly, always stroking in the direction of the grain. But be careful to avoid rubbing the chequering and the corners. It is wise to work through at least three grades of sand paper, taking time with each grade. The pad of sand paper should always be laid flat on the stock in the right hand whilst the left hand can be placed on top of the right to exert additional pressure if needed. As an alternative the sand paper can be wrapped around a cork block obtainable from DIY shops.

This type of careful sanding should easily remove minor scratches and marks but take great care to stop sanding when the stock is quite smooth; you must only remove the least amount of surface. It is also advisable to protect the metal parts with masking tape or at least sellotape.

The 'head' of the stock, where it joins the rear of the action body, and the edges of the recesses for lockplates, as well as the carved 'drop points' or panels, need the most care since they must retain their original sharp corners. Very careful work, with fine sand paper wrapped over a flat file or thin block of wood, is needed with these features.

Having prepared the wood, which should now look much lighter and natural, it is time to 'raise the grain' of the wood. Remove it from the vice and

5. Step Two. After the steel wool change to a suitable grade of glass paper.

6. Step Three. A small propane torch to help to dry the wood after it has undergone the wetting process.

sprinkle water sparingly all over the sand-papered area of the wood. This done the stock is then gently passed through the heat of a fire or naked flame. Take great care only to warm away the water rather than dry it too quickly and you must also avoid scorching the wood.

Once the stock is again quite dry, replace the action in the vice and rub the entire surface over lightly with very fine sand or glass paper. Repeat this until you can run your hand over the stock which now feels perfectly smooth.

Make absolutely sure that the stock really is *perfectly* smooth before continuing because this is the foundation on which the final finish is to be laid and on this smoothness will depend the whole appearance and feel of the finished stock. All scratches from earlier sandings must be removed and a little linseed oil on the paper in the final sanding may help. If the grain has not been fully raised then a trade filler can now be applied.

You should now be able to hold the stock at eye level and look across its surface at a light source and see no unsightly flats or high or low spots, no scratches or dents – just a perfectly level surface.

7.   Step Four. A little oil on the stock and rub into the wood using the fingers or a piece of clean rag.

8.   Step Five. The hand acts as a buff and in time a sheen will start to appear – but remember, there are no shortcuts and you must follow the process carefully.

9.   Step Six.   For French or button polish, apply linseed oil first
with a small piece of cotton so as to stop the button polish
becoming sticky.

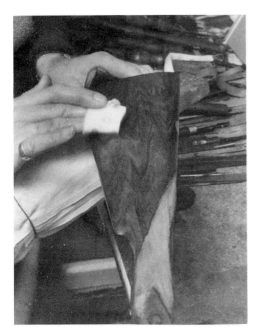

10.   Now use the cloth to apply the button polish quickly and
evenly. Start with small circles changing to long strokes with the
grain, but avoid the chequering.

Recolouring

Returning the stock to its original colour will invariably be necessary if the original finish has been completely removed. The proper recolouring of the stock (and indeed its final finish) needs just as much, if not more, care than the stages preceding it. Few things reveal the work of the non-professional so much as a stock of a 'wrong' colour or one with a patchy finish.

There are a number of choices for use as a recolouring medium. Firstly, discard the idea of anything described as a wood 'stain' or varnish. These preparations will normally seal the surface and prevent further colouring or finishing. Water-based stains will cause the grain to rise again due to their water content.

Wood dyes such as 'Colron' are the most commonly encountered in the DIY shops. These are normally 'spirit' based and will not usually affect the grain. With very careful test mixings of different colours, preferably tried out on an old stock, a satisfactory shade can be arrived at.

There is however no single colour which will duplicate the generally accepted and traditional shade as well as mixtures using alkanet root dye. This colouring agent has been used for countless years in the gun trade and, whether by familiarity or genuine superiority (it matters not which), will give almost any density of high- or low-grade French walnut the colour which both the tradesman and the client expect.

Alkanet root, in its raw state, looks rather like twigs or small branches cut into handy lengths of 6 inches or so. These are tipped into the linseed oil and turpentine mixture to release their unique colour over a period of days. Warming the pan helps accelerate the dye release, but beware of even approaching boiling, since (once warmed) too much linseed oil has the peculiar property of 'self heat generation' and a pan of this liquid on the stove will provide a 'chip pan fire' to remember for many a day. It is becoming increasingly difficult to find alkanet root dye and some foreign makers have found alternatives. There are however one or two ready-mixed stock finishes which include the dye.

Before starting on the final finish, ensure that all dust is removed from the stock's surface and that there is no chance that it can float back to turn the polish gritty.

The combined dye/polish mixture can either be applied daily with a paint brush but if colour only is to be added to the stock a clean cotton pad dipped into the mixture can be applied with even, long strokes until a satisfactory shade is obtained. Remember that the more coats of dye you add the darker the stock will become and that the polish skin you later add will deepen the colour too. Gently rub down the stock's surface to remove any 'whiskers' which might have been raised from the grain whilst recolouring and check again that no dust lies on the surface.

You can now apply whichever finish you have chosen from those described earlier, in the reasonable expectation of a stock of which you can be proud and which is largely due to proper and thorough preparation of the wood.

After an 'English' oil finish a final work over with a clean chamois leather and 'rotten stone' powder can be recommended to gloss and harden the stock's surface, but avoid the chequering.

The rotten stone powder, coupled with friction, creates heat which helps the oil to harden. An alternative but slightly less effective method is to use the palm of the hand to buff or cut the pumice powder on the stock.

The fore-end wood will probably need a similar treatment and even though it may not have any surface damage it is unlikely that the finish of the stock and the fore-end will match after refinishing the stock. Although smaller the fore-end wood deserves exactly the same care and attention in its refinishing. However in this case, depending on its type, the wood is removed from the metal to avoid scratching the blued parts.

Many modern stocks are supplied with a factory finish which is either a type of varnish or polyurethane. Generally the wood used will seldom repay the hard work entailed which has just been described. Nonetheless even the most uninteresting piece of wood can respond to thorough smoothing and refinishing, since it is unlikely that much care has been lavished on the wood before. Some surprisingly expensive guns have a surface which, to the trained eye of a skilled stock finisher, looks like the roof of a corrugated-iron shed!

To replace the varnish finish if it is scratched and chipped, perhaps by barbed wire, means chemically stripping off the old varnish completely then smoothing and revarnishing. A less satisfactory idea is to varnish over the scratches which at least prevents moisture entering the wood.

Re-chequering

The chequering on stock and fore-end has two purposes; one is to prevent the stock from slipping or turning in the hand, the other is decoration. Whilst the pattern cut at the small of the stock is undoubtedly functional, the chequering on a traditional splinter fore-end on a side-by-side gun is not since in almost all circumstances it is incorrect to grip the fore-end wood when shooting. This of course is not the case with a 'beaver tail' fore-end or the fore-end on most over-and-under, semi-automatic and 'pump' or 'slide' action guns.

So, whilst there used to be a few guns made which the owners preferred to be entirely free of chequering, today it is generally regarded as safer to have chequering present. Whilst some extremely pleasing, complicated and sometimes ostentatious chequering can be found on many imported guns, on English guns rather plain, formal designs based on a succession of straight lines in diamond or star shape are considered the norm.

The chequered areas of the small of the stock and the fore-end wood may have become worn or may have dents or bare patches in them. Also, inevitably, chequering retains dirt and grease as well as old stock polish and can simply need cleaning out.

Cleaning out and sharpening up the chequering should be well within the capability of any amateur gunsmith provided care is taken, the proper tools are chosen and the job is not rushed.

Chequering comes in three basic forms. The cheapest, reserved for the least expensive guns, is machine pressed into the wood. The next best is actually cut by machinery which can also be chased or finished off by hand afterwards. The best is marked out and cut by hand using a chequering tool. This too is graded according to the quality of the gun it adorns and ranges from rather coarse, with eight to ten lines per inch, to medium having fourteen to sixteen lines per inch. Fine chequering, having twenty to twenty-four lines per inch or more, takes the longest time and greater skill due to its closer lines. This grade is normally reserved for the high-quality gun.

11.   Chequering is a highly skilled job, needing specialised tools, and is probably best left to the expert. But you can attempt to clean out existing chequering provided you use the proper tool which has the correct number of teeth to match your gun's chequering pattern. Afterwards apply a little gunstock oil with a brush.

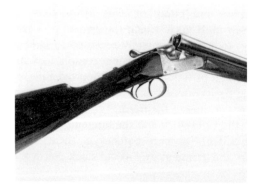

12.   You can now savour the satisfaction of a job well done.

Whilst it is courting disaster to attempt to mark out and *originate* chequering, cleaning out and sharpening simply needs the proper chequering tool. This is normally a thin cranked file with only two rows of teeth at its head, which has a 'pitch' or width of cut, i.e. between the two rows of teeth, which exactly matches the 'pitch' or number of lines per inch of the chequering on your stock.

An alternative tool, to clean out chequering, is an old three-cornered Swiss file ground sharp on two faces at an angle which will fit the angle of your chequering grooves.

With both these types of tool the method is quite similar. With the chequering tool start from one edge, locate the teeth of the tool in an outer parallel line and with smooth, gentle forward strokes work down the line to the end but stopping about ¼″ short of the border. Move into the next line locating one of the two teeth in the last groove and so work your way across the pattern.

As an unskilled amateur it is unwise to try to finish one whole chequering pattern at one attempt since, if you lose concentration and break across into the next row, the points taken off cannot be replaced. It is much better to do six lines and put the stock away till tomorrow than try for twelve lines and ruin the last pair. Better still, practise for some time on an old stock until the dexterity needed is acquired so that you can then confidently tackle the real thing.

It is worth repeating that you should not work right up to either border but should finish the last ¼″ by working *inwards* from the border to finish off. This will prevent unsightly over-runs or nicks outside the chequered panel.

Frequently you will find that external border lines are thicker than the inner chequering. Take equal care to use a specially shaped scraping tool to clean them out, as there are no shortcuts to doing the job thoroughly and properly.

The ground three-cornered file is used in much the same way, and when finished the chequering should be brushed out smartly and some stock finishing mixture used to seal it from damp and return its colour.

Finally, remember that (particularly in the case of the 'small' of the stock) each time it is re-chequered, the stock is slightly weakened and the chequering on each side of the stock is closer to meeting. So under no circumstances cut deeply when re-chequering, since the intention is only to clean out the grooves not deepen them appreciably.

CHAPTER EIGHT

Buying a Second-hand Gun

One of the nice aspects of shooting is buying a new gun!

It need not necessarily be brand new, since a well-made gun should give a lifetime's service and realise a very good second-hand value in the future. Unlike motor cars, electrical equipment (and almost anything else you care to mention), a well-made shotgun should not deteriorate with age. In fact, if properly cleaned and cared for, it should increase in value over the years.

There is however, like any other second-hand purchase, always an element of risk, both financial and physical. What might appear to the layman to be a perfectly sound weapon could well have a serious hidden defect or weakness which renders it at best, worth substantially less in value or, at worst, makes it a positive death trap!

All too often guns are offered for sale by people with little or no knowledge of the mechanical or safety aspects of a gun, so in case there is a serious defect, of which the seller is unaware, you should always try to buy from a reputable gunsmith or take any gun offered privately to an expert for an opinion of its safety and value.

It has to be recognised however that more and more guns are nowadays purchased by other methods. Some are bought from local auction rooms, others acquired from shooting-pals or maybe through a local newspaper advertisement. Obviously it is possible to buy exactly the gun you are looking for at an exceptionally good price by this method, but, due to your anxiety to snatch up a bargain, you might well be treading a veritable minefield of possible risks.

I will explain each method individually.

Auctions

What never fails to surprise me is the lack of information offered to the purchaser on guns that are entered in local auctions. The gun and fishing tackle sale (auction of sporting goods) has become increasingly popular in recent times. Indeed such an auction often makes an enjoyable afternoon or evening out with the opportunity to pick up the odd bargain, even a new gun.

To many auctioneers a 'sporting goods' sale is just another extension of their business which might also include selling furniture, antiques and so on. Obviously the well-known auction houses such as Christie's and Sotheby's as well as the arms auctioneers like Weller & Dufty and Wallis & Wallis, who have specialist weapon and sporting auctions, are usually well aware of the needs of prospective buyers.

But the smaller local sales offer virtually no back-up service whatsoever. I had a friend who was interested in buying an old English gun which he knew was to be included in a forthcoming auction. He contacted the auctioneers who were only able to tell him the make of the gun, and the fact that it was a 12 bore sidelock. But that was all!

It is by no means unknown for many of the guns entered into a 'sporting goods' sale to be consigned 'en bloc' to a local gun repairer who is paid a fixed price per gun for a quick cheap face-lift. This usually consists of blacking the barrels and a fairly superficial stock polish to make it shine temptingly.

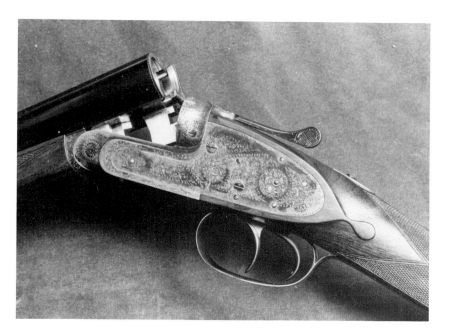

It is still possible to pick up a nice gun in an auction – but it is much easier to make a purchase you'll regret.

Things to look for are a pair of freshly blacked barrels and a glossy stock, whereas the rest of the gun's parts are dull and showing wear.

Within only a few weeks' use any pair of barrels will show silvered wear on the high spots, particularly at muzzle and chamber's ends, caused simply by being carried and returned to the gun slip or case. Similarly a stock which has been used must show some slight wear particularly near the 'small' or 'hand' of the stock. This does not necessarily mean that a gun which has obviously been 'tarted up' is dangerous but such a gun should be given closer scrutiny than others which show only honest wear.

At the end of this chapter is a simple check list which should perhaps be adopted as standard practice at all local sporting sales – and also a check list for potential purchases. As you will see, there is much which can be wrong with a gun. It is far too easy to waste your money *and* put your health at risk. So first and foremost, if you intend buying a gun at an auction (and there is no reason why you shouldn't) then take all possible precautions and visit the sale room for the 'viewing'.

Don't rub your hands with glee when you notice that the actual sale is held in the evening and that you needn't take time off from your work. If you are going to buy a gun, take that time off and get to the viewing which means turning up at least one or two hours before the sale starts and the guns on offer are being handled by other prospective buyers like you. You will then get an opportunity to make the numerous checks that should be made before you decide what to bid for.

Proof

Firstly buy the booklet *Notes on Proof* sold by both the London and Birmingham proof houses and get to know the rules!

If BP alone is stamped on the flats then my advice is to proceed no further as this denotes Black Powder proofing only. Such a gun, built to handle black powder, may not pass the nitro proof test! And even if it bears the marks BNP (Birmingham Nitro Proof) it may well have been in use for over sixty years with all that potential wear and tear.

Keep very firmly in mind that the proof marks visible only indicate that *at the time of original manufacture and proof* the gun had passed the safety test which was laid down by law at that time. For further details about proof turn to the next chapter.

But if, for instance, the chamber length (e.g. $2\frac{1}{2}''$) is stamped on the barrel flats it will probably have been proofed since 1925, and if the service pressure (in tons per square inch) is shown the barrels will have been submitted to and passed proof since the 1954 rules came into force.

The barrels are obviously one of the most vital areas for your attention but you must first learn to 'view' a pair of barrels properly rather than just look through them – there is quite a difference!

Hold the barrels up at eye level at about 45 degrees and point towards a constant, diffused light source, i.e. normal daylight on an overcast day. Do *not* point into the sun or an electric light bulb, both of which will dazzle your eyes.

Position the tubes a few inches from your eyes and *keep both eyes open*, i.e. do not squint, so that you can actually focus on the near as well as the far end. Putting the muzzles almost against your eyes will prevent you from focussing on the first few inches of the bores. Neither should you peer through the barrels at the circles of light at the far end since this will tell you nothing of potential flaws to the bores in the distance between. So always look *into* the barrels rather than through them and keep both eyes open!

Pivoting the barrels on your left hand, which should be half way up the tubes, describe a shallow circle with the barrels. This will throw a shadow down the inside walls and betray any dents or 'rivelling' (corrugations or 'waves') in the walls. If you spot any suspicious marks turn the barrels to different angles and concentrate your attention on that spot. View from both ends of the barrels to confirm the mark as a dent, bulge or whatever it might be.

Pitting will be fairly easy to spot but a dent or bulge should have a corresponding mark on the outside of the barrels. Put your finger on where the mark appears to be whilst still looking down the bore which should help locate its counterpart on the outside.

Viewing the outside of the barrels, often called 'shadow viewing', means holding the barrels in the same way but looking over the top of them and tipping them to throw a thin shadow down the outside wall. If the shadow is broken the chances are there is a dent or bulge at that point. Invariably this will coincide with a mark in the bore. If you own the gun put a piece of sticky tape onto the mark, so that you can easily find it again, and take the barrels to a competent gunsmith. Continue your inch-by-inch search of the tubes, expecting to find most trouble in the last foot of barrels, i.e. at the front or muzzle end where the tubes are thinnest.

You will also need to take the bore measurements and calculate if they are in proof and by how much. This measurement is taken nine inches from the breech or chamber end using a special measuring tool. One such tool is supplied by Chubbs of Edgware. The auctioneers should at least have a gunsmith present as their resident expert for the sale and he can be approached to check the gun for you. Sadly however this is not always the case.

The first 12″ of the barrels are the strongest and obviously the muzzle end is the weakest so you will also need to check the barrel wall thickness. Unfortunately there is no existing recommendation for barrel wall thickness, and different makers produce barrels of differing dimensions. Strangely it is often the case that the beautifully made, higher-quality gun has the thinnest barrel walls to start with. This is due to paring away unwanted weight to produce the sleek, well-balanced, lightweight, thoroughbred gun which is a dream to handle. But as a result, a few dents raised and some minor lapping to remove light pitting, can render the gun potentially dangerous. As a rough yardstick never entertain a gun with barrel walls less than 24 thou. thick since the next dent will probably render them dangerous. On the other hand excessive barrel wall thickness can adversely affect the game gun's weight and balance.

I well remember going to buy a Purdey for a customer. It was a very handsome gun, well in proof and it looked every inch a very good buy – but a subsequent report showed that the barrels were only 20 thou. thick! – due no doubt to the refinishing mentioned in the previous paragraphs.

It would probably have been quite safe to use – indeed there are countless similar guns in active service many in far worse condition than that one. But I never take chances, particularly with something as potentially dangerous as a shotgun. The strength of the barrels will depend on whether dents have been taken out of them, how they have been taken out and the method and expertise used in the 'striking up' of the barrels afterwards.

There is only one way to judge a barrel wall thickness and that is by measuring it and, naturally, there is a special tool for measuring this too! On average a new gun should have barrel walls of at least 25–26 thou. thick.

Another obvious flaw to look for on the inside of the bores is pitting or very bad dents. Pitting is invariably caused by neglect, i.e. dirt left in the bores has held moisture, thus creating the pits (corrosion) sometimes dotted around both the inside and the outside of the barrels. In guns of older manufacture this was frequently caused by 'corrosive primers'. In the old days cartridges were fitted with detonating caps which used 'fulminate of mercury'. Whilst this was quite reasonably efficient as a detonating compound, the chemical released began corroding the bores within a few hours. So a gun not cleaned immediately after use was rusty inside by the next day. Any pitting on the outside of a pair of barrels is caused by simple neglect. At some stage in its life it has been left standing in a damp room or worse still an outhouse. Another less obvious hazard is to store a gun in a baize-lined compartment case for any length of time. The baize can absorb atmospheric moisture and transfer it to the barrels over a period of months. Guns are best stored either in an open gun rack or in a glazed cabinet.

Pitting bored or 'lapped' from the inside enlarges the bore – likewise metal smoothed from the outside reduces the barrel wall thickness. So you can see why you need to check the barrel wall thickness carefully in the first place. Guns may not have always been well cared for by some previous owner.

The worrying thing about pitting is that it is usually an unknown quantity. It could simply be superficial or it may have bitten deeply. You may have to make an on-the-spot judgement so if you are in any doubt – leave well alone!

A barrel may have suffered only a slight dent but at some point it may have been in the hands of an unskilled amateur who has inadvertently rendered the gun 'out of proof' during the process of raising the dent.

Many guns have been put out of proof in this way. Raising a dent is a fairly common occurrence and is a routine job to a skilled gunsmith, but it is a job best entrusted to an experienced barrel worker. It involves the use of a plug or 'hydraulic dent raiser' being placed inside the barrel under the dent which provides an anvil as the dent is eased out by gentle tapping on the barrel in the area immediately around the dent.

You should never use a gun with any sort of obstruction in the bore, not even the slightest dent or bulge. Even this slight obstruction could possibly cause the barrels to burst – with pieces of metal flying about!

Whilst also on the subject of the barrels look closely for 'rivels'. This is a series of slight corrugations on the inside of the bore, often quite difficult to detect, which is caused by the pressure wave which follows a shot charge up the barrel. The barrel wall always bulges when a shot is fired but in the case of 'rivelling' the wall stretches too much and does not return to its former diameter properly.

'Rivelling' is usually a symptom of thin barrel walls, an overloaded cartridge, a minor obstruction, like a bit of cleaning cloth, or even an excess of oil left in the barrels can cause it. *Always* clean out the oil from the barrels of any gun before firing.

A loose rib is another potential hazard. A loose top rib or indeed the bottom rib can be most easily detected by hanging the barrels by the lump hook from your forefinger and tapping them against the side of the wood bench (or smartly with a pencil). There should be a clear ring like a bell. But if there is a dull tone or any 'buzzing' vibration the chances are that one of the several soldered parts of the barrel has come loose. If this happens the joints between the ribs, fore-end loop and the barrels should be cleaned out thoroughly. With the aid of a small $3\times$ or $6\times$ magnifying glass, examine the rib joints inch by inch. Rust, or minute 'pin holes' in the soldered joints, may be detected and there may also be rust fizzing away inside the cavity between the barrels. Relaying loose ribs is a job for a skilled repairer. Also check the condition of the barrel loop, the part on which the fore-end fastens.

Another important thing to look for is to see if the barrels and action are perfectly tight and the gun is what is described in gunsmiths' parlance as being 'on the face'. This simply means that there are no appreciable gaps between the chamber end of the barrels and the face of the action, nor gaps between the barrel flats and the flats of the action bar.

This can be checked visually by holding the gun above your eyes against a strong light source. If an appreciable amount of light can be seen creeping through the joint between the breech or the flats then there is cause for concern. Another test is to try to slide pieces of different thickness paper between the barrels and action at the face and between the flats.

In an old gun this probably means that tightening of the barrels to the action has been done – but only superficially! If it is a newish gun, the gun was not jointed i.e. assembled properly when it was made.

You can also discover if a gun has become loose by a simple 'vibration' test. Remove the fore-end from the assembled gun, take the small of the stock in the right hand, place the end of the stock on your thigh and shake the barrels. Any looseness will be transmitted through the gun as a distinct vibration.

If the action appears to be tight on the barrels, it might have been done only to effect a quick sale. Look for signs of hammer marks in the edge of the semi-circle of the hook on the front barrel lump and in the 'bites' which take the bolt. Has the action been deliberately squeezed in a vice to effect a temporary tightness which will quickly loosen after purchase?

A new piece may have been brazed or a dove-tailed piece let into the semi-circle in the front lumps to tighten a loose action – but done properly this is a perfectly acceptable repair to a well-used gun.

Whilst mentioning brazing it is well worth remembering that, in the case of even an inexpensive English gun, the lumps are usually brazed in place whereas the ribs and other ancillary parts are 'tinned'. This makes the removal or relaying of a loose ('sprung') rib a fairly simple matter.

In the case of many imported guns the lumps, ribs etc. are all brazed into place at the same time. Due to the high temperature needed to liquify brazing, as compared to the relatively low temperature of 'tinning', taking a rib off or trying to re-lay it can cause difficulties due to heat distortion. For a seriously damaged gun, sleeving or new barrels are the only answer. Brazed barrels are easily recognised by yellow metal joining the ribs etc. Tinning is a silver colour.

A side-to-side shaking movement could also prove similarly revealing. You might also detect tell-tale vibrations by striking the stock with the palm of your left hand with your other hand's thumb and forefinger clasping the joint to feel movement between the barrel ends and the action face. The commonly used expression for this vibration is 'headache' and a gun which betrays such movement is said to 'have a headache'.

Another feature of the barrels, that is sometimes accidentally overlooked, is their length. The gun may be advertised as having 27" barrels and to all appearances is a nice-looking, but oldish, English gun. But, as in the case of many older guns, it may once have had 30" barrels which have been shortened and 'modernised' by removing 3" from the end of the barrels and taken away much, if not all, of the chokes in the process!

This kind of alteration can only be detected if you check the choke both by looking very carefully and measuring the muzzles. Remember that, at present, the auctioneer is under no legal obligation to say whether or not the gun has any choke or if it has chokes what they actually are. Few auctioneers would know how to measure choke!

It is far too late once the gun has been bought – choke is something which can be easily removed from the barrels by boring out or shortening, but is not so easily replaced.

But even though the barrels may have been butchered by having most, if not all, of the chokes cut off, all is not necessarily lost. Provided the barrel walls are thick enough a skilled barrel borer may be able to 'recess' bore some choke back into the barrels. However, this method, which effectively creates a 'cylinder' in the walls behind the muzzles, even if possible, can guarantee no more than $1/2$ choke in either barrel. But, properly bored, polished, patterned and regulated a game gun throwing say $1/2$ choke left and improved cylinder right can be hoped for. Naturally, this highly specialised work must be added to the cost of the basic price paid for the gun.

Another alteration which might have taken place is that the chambers could have been deepened. The most common modernising alteration of this kind is converting a $2^1\!/_2$"-chambered gun to $2^3\!/_4$" chambers. Such a change needs the gun to be reproofed. Alas, this is not always done, and such a gun, if fired unknowingly, could be very dangerous. So check whether there are first proof and reproof marks. Look especially for the defacement of proof marks, usually a series of criss-crossed lines done with a cold chisel edge. It must be emphasised that under no circumstances should you purchase a gun if any part of the proof marks appears to have been removed or defaced. No matter how tempting a bargain it might appear to be, it may be completely beyond economic and safe repair. Never forget that an unsafe gun can be extremely dangerous!

Some years ago I was offered a pair of Holland & Holland sidelocks in their original case. They had been shortened so that most of the choke was removed – who could guess what kind of pattern would be thrown and was the gun recess choke bored and regulated afterwards? Only a session at the pattern plate would tell the true story and an enquiry of the makers to see if they have a record in the gun register.

The poor chap who had bought them was completely unaware of the fact that they were altered. When I pointed this out to him, to say he was surprised is an understatement. The missing inches, and particularly the missing chokes, have a significant effect on the value of the guns.

A high proportion of older guns, mainly those made before or at the turn of the century, had 30" or even 32" barrels. Many of these have been shortened but there are three features to look for in detecting them. One is that these guns had top ribs reminiscent of the old muzzle loaders and, if you look carefully, are noticeably broader than modern, even flat file cut, ribs.

The second 'give away' feature, shared with a modern gun which has been shortened, is that careful examination of the muzzles, as if looking down the barrels, will reveal that the tubes do not actually touch each other in the middle as they should. The two roughly triangular steel fillers fitted in the two spaces between the top and bottom ribs and the inside of the barrels may have been supplemented with a new soldered-in plug between the tubes themselves.

The third feature which, once you are familiar with the 'right' or 'wrong' feel or appearance of a gun, is that, looked at from above, the muzzles seem unnaturally wide. In extreme cases, particularly if 32" barrels are shortened to 28", the barrels look as if they are almost parallel. Where the centre of the pattern would then strike is a matter of speculation!

It is also worth remembering that in older guns the complete length of the chokes, including their cones or 'lead', was up to 4" long whereas in more recent times the same chokes and their cones are normally confined to the last 2" of the barrels. So a shortening by 2" may or may not remove all the original choke.

Whilst speaking of barrels, and their building, it is interesting to note that barrels are joined, after being carefully packed with shims of tin and wired before soldering, so that an imaginary line taken down the centre of each bore will cross at 40 yards distance. This obviously governs the 'point of impact' or more accurately the centre of the pattern.

There are many who get caught out in this way. But it's simple enough to check. It's just that in the tense atmosphere of an auction room the person bidding might not have been thorough in his viewing of the gun and, in the excitement of the bidding, all he could think about was the bargain that was about to come his way! There are no winners or losers in a sale-room so when you conduct your examination of any gun that you are contemplating buying check the chokes and the chambers particularly carefully.

You can buy a simple choke gauge. J. R. Clark's make a very nice brass one, that can also be used as a key ring fob. And for checking the chambers, use a slender 6" rule. Slide it down into the chamber of the barrels close against the wall. You will then feel the rule stop at the lead-in. Put your thumb at the relevant point on the rule and read the measurement.

Stock and fore-end

Another common mistake made at auctions is the buying of a gun with a cracked stock.

There is no point in believing that a cracked stock could last several years. It could just as easily give way in a matter of hours.

Once a piece of wood is cracked there is no miracle known to mankind which will make the grain stitch itself back together as if it were human bone. Glue will stick wood together, but it can never be completely relied upon. Recoil and vibration have a nasty habit of prying open brittle glue joints. Wooden dowel pegs or specially made nuts and bolts are a feasible but seldom attractive possibility.

So watch for tell-tale signs of the head of the stock (immediately behind the action) being pinned or dowel pegs fitted as this area is often prone to splitting, and the former owner may be tempted to have it pinned or dowel pegged to hold it together rather than fit a new stock.

It's a simple enough job, and the gun will look reasonably decent and the pin or pegs can be concealed by plugs or chequering so why worry? The answer is simple – what starts as a small crack can finish as a big one, and there is very little you can do about it.

The decision either to pin or dowel a piece of wood or to buy a gun that has a pinned or dowel pegged stock may be made when one's judgement is clouded – either by a low price or you are attracted by a very nicely figured piece of walnut in the butt.

So having borne in mind that it is unusual to find a properly mended stock, your next step will be to consider how much it might cost to have a new stock made and fitted to the gun. Go to two or three shops for quotes and you could quickly discover that your bargain is no longer a bargain. Even the cheapest quote may make the restocked gun more costly than another gun with a sound original stock. The only solution therefore is to buy the gun at the right price and then have it restocked, but *do your sums first!*

The final part of your checklist of the woodwork will be to examine for any sign of oil saturation. While it is wise to keep a gun properly maintained and free of rust, some people go absolutely overboard with the oil, and the consequence is soft and spongy wood that you can push your thumb nail into which is of little use for the purpose intended.

Close examination of the chequering on the stock and fore-end will reveal whether the wear present is in keeping with a gun which had a normal working life or one which has been misused and abused over a short or long period.

Action

We now come to the nitty gritty of the moving parts!

First, let us look at the ejectors. People often like to open a gun with great gusto and watch the empty cases eject; it might look impressive but it will tell you nothing about the effectiveness and timing of the ejector work. Make sure you check the ejectors properly. Check the timing of the ejectors so that by opening the gun very slowly and tapping the stock down a fraction at a time the ejectors can work completely of their own volition. Listen carefully and you may hear a 'click-click' close together: this is the ejectors cocking just before the cases fly out. They should leave the chambers in perfect unison *not* one after the other. Neither should they hit the face of the action on the way out. The slower you work the ejectors the more likely they are to show a defect.

Ejector problems are some of the most common that gunsmiths have to deal with. If the gun is not a current mass-produced model, then new parts will almost certainly have to be made by hand. The cost of the repair may be expensive.

Often a gun responds quite differently to snap caps than to cartridges being fired. So if there is a slight problem with ejecting the snap caps you can assume that there may be a bigger problem when firing a live cartridge. Remember . . . a snap cap might tell you some of the story, but it has no recoil and it cannot be expected to tell you everything.

Feel your way around the gun. Trigger pulls are another critical consideration so squeeze them gently with the snap caps in. You will then tell whether they are heavy, light, hair trigger or working perfectly satisfactorily. The worst event is when you pull the trigger and nothing happens. This can mean that the sear (the part which releases the internal hammer) does not lift out of the bent of the hammer.

Malfunctions of this type are much more common on cheaper imported guns. The metal used might be soft or may not have been properly heat treated. This is only one of the many reasons why such guns are cheaper in the first place. There is nothing necessarily wrong with their basic design, but economies have to be made somewhere for them to be made and sold cheaply.

Production-line gunmaking is obviously one of the best price cutters and in principle this is fine. I was trained in the old school of a lot of work being done by hand using the basic skills, a minimum of machinery and hand tools.

But I have seen many of the big factory production lines in Europe and I was very impressed by them. Some are tooled up with very sophisticated machines that work to extremely fine tolerances and obviously produce very fine guns at their price.

Further savings on guns can be made by using substandard materials – bland uninteresting wood and soft metal – and also by a lack of attention to detail on finish and this applies to more than just the exterior work. The finish and filing of the interior working parts of the action is where the economies show up most but, of course, you don't see them till the gun breaks down. Some makes, specialising in cheap, mass-produced guns, are particularly prone to trigger and ejector problems. I've seen some real horrors in my time!

Price

How do you decide how much to pay?

Scan advertisements in gun magazines for prices. Probably an even better guideline are catalogues from gun sales held by the many auction houses. A yearly subscription will entitle you to a series of catalogues, some giving 'estimated' price guides, i.e. what the auctioneer thinks a lot will or should realise. Each subsequent catalogue almost invariably lists prices actually realised in the previous sale.

The name of the gunmaker will often influence the price that the gun fetches at auction but the condition that the gun is in will also have an effect on the price paid. It is obviously wiser to buy a sound, well-built gun by a provincial maker than a best London gun which has been neglected or tampered with. The number of people attending an auction can also have a significant bearing on the figure realised but just two or three bidders wanting the same gun is all it takes to cause the price to rocket!

You will have attended the viewing and decided which gun you are after. Work out beforehand what you are prepared to pay – and do not go beyond that price. It is all too easy to become over-excited in the competitive atmosphere of the sale-room and suddenly find that you have committed yourself to spending far more money than you intended.

Visit two or three auctions empty-handed just to get the feel of how they work. At each sale pick out the gun which you would most like to buy, fix your own price limit and follow the bidding through without yourself making a bid. You can then see how close you were to judging the right price and you will know what to expect when you actually decide to bid, but remember to take along your shotgun certificate otherwise you cannot take the gun away!

Buying from an advert in a newspaper

Much of the same advice applies but also bear in mind . . .

1. Shotgun certificates – you need to see each other's to effect a legal sale.

2. If you arrange a meeting, and it transpires that the gun is out of proof, the vendor should be made aware that he is liable to a fine of up to £1000 per barrel for selling a gun which is out of proof.

3. Arranging a sale by meeting in a public house car park is quite popular, as a mutually convenient rendezvous but, it would be much better to meet at a local shooting ground where you can examine the gun and try it out on a few clays before deciding to buy.

4. It may be that by coincidence you know the person who responds to your advertisement or he is known to a mutual friend. On the other hand should a complete stranger telephone be cautious and *do not* give him your address. He could well be a criminal looking for a worthwhile place to make an uninvited call. If a transaction does take place ensure you have his name, address and telephone number and the details from his shotgun certificate.

Buying from a gunshop

Similar rules apply. You will need to ascertain the bore size, the barrel wall thickness, the chambers and a proper description of what you are thinking of buying.

Inspect the gun just as carefully as you would before an auction sale or if buying a gun from a stranger. If you were taking a gun in to sell the gunshop proprietor would want to carry out the same kind of inspection himself. Don't be put off by being self-conscious – it is *your* hard-earned money and *your* health which are at stake. Even a gun selling cheaply is hardly likely to be so cheap nowadays. By law the gunshop proprietor has to enter any sale in a register against your name and address, so make sure that what you are buying is exactly what it appears to be.

The vast majority of well-established gunshops can be trusted to offer a fair deal but the problem is that almost anyone can start a gunshop which, within a few weeks, may appear to be a perfectly sound and reputable business. Honest and well intentioned though they may be, its proprietor(s) may have little idea of offering the kind of experienced technical advice you are entitled to expect.

A few discreet enquiries of the local shooting community can help establish how long a shop has been open and the kind of reputation it has for fair prices and fair deals.

The point which needs emphasising is that you are *not* being unreasonable when seeking safeguards – you are entitled to be sure of exactly what you are buying.

In most circumstances the gunshop is the most reliable way to purchase a second-hand gun. At least you have somewhere to take the gun back to and you will usually find that most reputable shops will be only too happy to correct any fault which may develop soon after you have made your purchase, sometimes giving a 6- or 12-months guarantee.

Another advantage with a gunshop purchase is that with a written invoice provided by a gunshop, giving full details of the gun and the purchase price, you can then go to your insurance agent or broker and arrange the appropriate cover for the gun. Incidentally, always try to arrange that the insured value of the gun increases from year to year. This will perhaps save you having to pay for another insurance valuation in a few years' time.

The best advice I can give is to find a good gunshop or gunmaker and stick with them. If you keep to one gunmaker he will most likely be able to find you the type of gun you are looking for, even if you have to wait a couple of months. The short wait may well be worth it in the long term, because he will use his skill and judgement to obtain a gun for you that he knows will suit your particular needs.

Build up this kind of relationship and become a regular customer and you then may have someone to turn to for expert advice if a bargain crops up in a local auction or newspaper advert.

Buying from a friend

In some ways this can be one of the most difficult ways of obtaining a gun since, due to your friendship, you are prevented from asking the searching questions necessary and the transaction has, to some degree, to be taken on trust. He may be a fellow syndicate member or shooting pal, but he may not know (and could not reasonably be expected to know) about the intricacies of a gun's finer points.

I would suggest that prior to purchase the gun be borrowed and discreetly taken to your local gunsmith where he can carry out the necessary checks. His report could prove enlightening and save your friend (the vendor) and you (the purchaser) much embarrassment in the long run.

In that way the friendship need not suffer but, on the other hand, if a purchase was made on trust which later turned out to be a mistake a good relationship could easily be spoiled. The small fee for a proper inspection by a gunsmith is a mere pittance when compared to what is actually at stake both in terms of the purchase and the value of the friendship itself.

Reasons for buying

Just before parting with your money – ask yourself whether this is *exactly* the gun that you were looking for. A good bargain should be a sound investment too and, as a bonus, it will give you the pleasure of acquisition and a pride in ownership.

Sadly, many guns are bought on impulse. The gun may happen to take your fancy or you may have borrowed it and, by chance, may have shot particularly well with it (an endearing quality in any gun). You might instead simply have been the victim of a bit of good salesmanship. It is also well worth bearing in mind that every worn-out old gun, taken in part exchange for a new one, has to be sold to someone. No one is likely to take it out to the back and put it in the dustbin – you could be the new owner of that 'tarted-up' gun if you are not careful.

So, when you decide you want another gun, decide *exactly* what you are looking for, give it a great deal of thought, be positive in your approach to its acquisition; you are then unlikely to have any regrets.

The two check lists which follow are those that I use when carrying out a detailed examination on behalf of a customer who asks me to check a gun with a view to purchase or who seeks a detailed valuation for private or insurance purposes.

The sporting gun sale list is the one I use for the benefit of an auction house who requires my services to view guns before they are placed in their sale.

You will note that the sheet has space for personal comments to be made that could be useful at a later date.

PROSPECTIVE PURCHASER'S CHECK LIST

MAKE:	GUN NO:	AGE:	GAUGE:

Barrels   *Comments*

Bore size L/barrel _____
Bore size R/barrel _____
Dents in barrels _____
Loose loop _____
Ribs loose _____
Choke borings _____
Chamber depth _____
Barrel wall thickness L/barrel _____
Barrel wall thickness R/barrel _____
First or second proof _____
Original or sleeved tubes _____
Type of barrel extension (doll's head, etc.) _____
Type of top rib _____

Action

Boxlock or sidelock _____
Ejector or non-ejector _____
Automatic or non-auto safety _____
Full hardening colours or silver action _____
Single or double trigger _____
Style of engraving _____
Gun tight or needs rejointing _____
General quality of all pins and slots _____
Ejector work functions correctly _____

Stock and Fore-end

Quality of wood _____
Straight hand stock _____
Full pistol grip _____
Half pistol grip _____
Cast for left or right handed _____
With or without drop points _____
Wood under or above metalwork _____
Bend at comb and heel _____
Stock length _____
Quality and condition of chequering _____
Condition of wood _____
Oil or French polished presentation _____
Splinter fore-end _____
Bevertail fore-end _____
With or without Anson-type push rod _____

SPORTING GUN SALE

MAKE:	GUN NO:	AGE:	GAUGE:

Type of Action

Sidelock
Boxlock
Over/under
Automatic/pump action

Length of Barrels

Original or sleeved. Tubes
Bore size left
Bore size right
Barrel wall thickness
First or second proof
Chamber length
Choke borings

Stock Configuration

Bend at comb and heel
Length of stock
Straight hand
Half or pistol grip
Quality of wood

Auction house statistics and comments

CHAPTER NINE

English Proof

The Gunmakers is one of the youngest of the City Livery Companies. Most of the Craft Guilds had already been founded prior to the year 1637 when the Gunmakers sought their Charter. At this time gunmaking was an established trade in the City of London.

The Charter was granted on 14 March 1637 and included the rights of view, gauge, proof, trial and marking of all hand guns including 'Dags' (a name used for heavy pistols) within a ten-mile radius of London.

At that time there was no official proof house in Birmingham. It was deemed by the Birmingham Gunsmiths that they were at a disadvantage and as a result of vigorous representation the Gun Barrel Proof Act of 1813 established a body known as the Guardians, Trustees and Wardens of the Gun Barrel Proof House of Birmingham.

Its purpose was that of 'proofing or causing to be proofed all barrels for guns, fowling pieces, blunderbusses, pistols and any other firearm that should be brought to the proof house at Birmingham'. Thus the Worshipful Company of Gunmakers (London) and the Guardians of the Birmingham proof house became the official bodies charged by Parliament to proof firearms and ensure that they are safe before they may be offered for sale.

Further acts of 1815, 1868 and 1950 changed and at the same time strengthened these powers. The Gun Barrel Proof Act of 1868 is, in the main, the current act. Certain provisions of this act have been revised by the act of 1950, which permits increases in the authorised maximum prices for proof.

Since the year 1813 it has been an offence to sell, or offer for sale, an unproved shotgun anywhere in the United Kingdom. Ignorance of the law is no excuse. These notes are designed to give the shooter an insight into the proofing of new and second-hand shotguns.

Both proofing and re-proofing necessitate the firing of an approximately 70 per cent heavier load through the barrel than is ever likely to be fired in normal circumstances. The proof load should and is intended to disclose any weaknesses in the gun. It is clearly better that the proof house discover any weakness thus reducing the risk of personal injury that may result. A 12 bore shotgun chambered for $2^3/4$ " cartridges has a service pressure of $3^1/4$ tons per square inch.

Provisional proof

The purpose of provisional proof is to ascertain that a barrel's tube is quite sound before the gunmaker expends too much labour on what could prove to be faulty material. The tube is roughly finished and bored but not chambered. The chamber end of the tube is fitted with a screwed plug which is inserted where the finished chamber will be. The plug is generally known as a 'hutt' (a relic of muzzle-loading terminology) and has a touch hole to fire the charge.

This is known as 'provisional' or 'first' proof and a small stamp is placed on the underside of the tube itself just forward of where the barrel flats will begin.

'Definitive' or 'final' proof

The assembled gun is submitted to this when almost finished. All the metal parts have been made and fitted although normally final polishing and blueing and blacking have yet to be done. The gun is then known as being 'in the white'.

Almost invariably the stock and fore-end wood is not fitted whilst proofing since both could be damaged during proof firing. The proof charge is normally made up using 'TSP' powder i.e. 'Tower Special Proof' gun-powder which is stored in a humidity-controlled cabinet to prevent variable pressures due to varying amounts of moisture (which controls the burning rate) being present in the powder.

In the case of a sidelock gun false side plates are fitted. These are to protect the action body when securing the gun in the special recoil carriage used by the proof house. Parts which are fitted include the top lever (but without its spring) and the spindle and bolt. Usually dummy firing pins are added which are struck by separate external hammers on firing. These are brought down by pulling a lanyard (string) from behind a reinforced glass screen.

Boxlock guns are submitted to proof only slightly differently. Their lever work, hammers and sears are also fitted but once more the woodwork is normally omitted to prevent the risk of damage in firing.

The rules of proof specify the loads to be used in the proof test together with the standards of view before and after provisional and definitive proof. Viewing, it must be emphasised, is the most critical part of the proof test.

Also detailed are the marks (or metal stamps) which have to be added to guns which pass proof. Details such as the bore, chamber dimension and pressure per square inch and, since the year 1970, the year of proof is also stamped on the barrel flats. The action bar flats also receive briefer but no less significant stamps.

These marks remain valid indefinitely or until any gun marked as proved has been altered or reduced in strength for example by significant enlargement of the bore or chamber. If the proof marks are accidentally removed or defaced the barrels or action instantly become unproved and resubmission to proof becomes necessary.

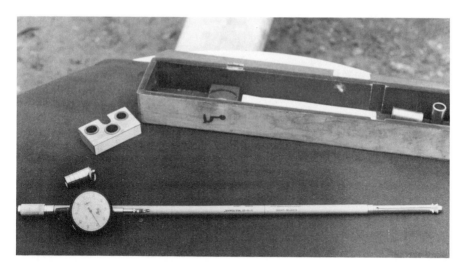

Bore measuring tool and choke gauge.

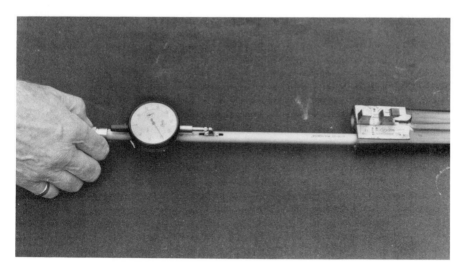

Bore measuring tool in use.

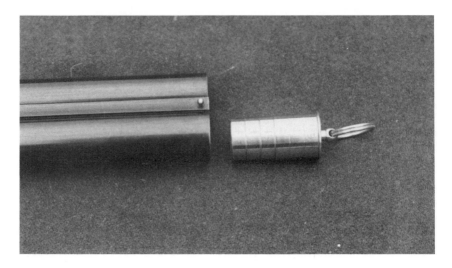

Choke gauge.

Re-proof

This may be necessary for a variety of reasons – there may be indications that the action has become weak or the barrel may be reduced in strength due to enlargement of the bore, excessive pitting, bulges, rivelling or any signs of cracks or flaws in the barrel. It might be that the barrels have brazed dovetailed lumps which now show signs of looseness. Even chopper lump barrels have been known to part very slightly. Many non-ejector guns have been successfully converted to ejector, which requires reproving since there might be a potential weakness due to enlargement of machined slots, holes etc. in the action or ejector leg holes.

Reproving is needed where welding has been used to execute a repair on either action or barrel, or where there has been a deepening of chambers for example from 2½″ to 2¾″ or from 2¾″ to 3″. Perhaps old barrels have been replaced with new, or other minor alterations have affected the strength of the gun.

The fitting of a multichoke or variable choke also necessitates reproof. And a black powder gun must not under any circumstances be used with modern nitro cartridges until having been subjected to nitro proof although, of course, black powder loaded cartridges can be used.

Any individual can submit a gun for proof at either of the proof houses, but usually it is far better that they submit the gun through a reputable gunsmith. Seldom is a gun presented for proof without some preparatory work having been carried out.

The gun must of course be 'on the face' (the action and barrels tight and well jointed) and the barrels must be free of any dents, rivelling or bulging in

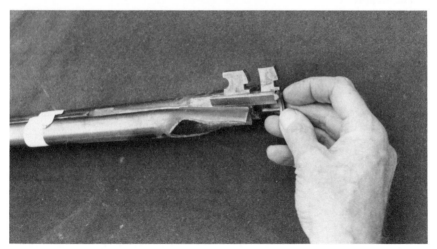

Don't take chances with old guns!

the bore. Pitting should be removed as far as possible.

The proof house will not accept any responsibility for damage arising from proof firing. So it *must* be remembered that guns submitted for reproof are submitted at their owner's risk.

If a gun is rejected or fails to withstand the proof test then in some circumstances it may be repaired and resubmitted. On the final rejection the existing proof marks will be defaced usually by criss-crossed chisel marks. If the gun has failed proof it is technically illegal for it to be sold and most certainly should never be used unless successfully proved again.

Then the most satisfactory solution is to render it completely unusable to ensure that it can never be used by some person who may be unaware of its unproved condition.

A very useful booklet is published by the proof houses entitled 'Notes on the Proof of Shotguns and other Small Arms'. For those who shoot, collect or even just handle guns this booklet is essential reading since it contains invaluable information.

It includes all the marks ever used by both Birmingham and London proof houses, and also shows the many foreign proof marks which are acceptable and valid, without reproof, in this country. In addition it specifies the foreign-made guns which *must* be proved, at either proof house, before they can legally be sold in Great Britain. This work and that of proving rifles, pistols, humane killers, etc. forms a large proportion of the work of both proof houses. Among its pages can be found advice on the purchase of second-hand shotguns, sale by auction and other useful data.

The book is available, at a small charge, from: The Proof House, 48 Commercial Road, London, or Birmingham Proof House, Banbury Street, Birmingham.

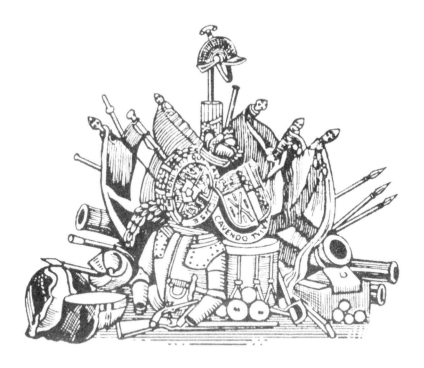

THE REPROOF OF SHOTGUNS

A memorandum issued jointly by
The Worshipful Company of Gunmakers of London
The Gun Trade Association Ltd.
The Guardians of the Birmingham Proof House

Proof is the testing required by law of a new shotgun (or other small arm) before sale, to ensure as far as is practicable, that it has adequate strength to stand up to the pressures and strains to which it will be subjected in normal use. Re-proof is the similar testing of a gun which has previously been proved. Proof and Re-proof of shotguns involve pressures between 60% and 80% higher than the established service pressure. For example, in a 12-bore $2^3/4''$ chambered gun the established service pressure is $3^1/4$ tons (7,280 lb) per square inch. The need for strength is evident.

If mishandled or neglected a gun may be weakened even during a short period of service so that, although it is marked as having been duly proved, it may have become out of Proof. Reliance on the Proof marks alone is therefore not sufficient. Early indications of weakness are often apparent only to those who have been trained to recognise them. Inspection of guns by a Gunmaker at regular intervals is advisable, and recommendation to submit for Re-proof should be followed without delay, to avoid undue risk of personal injury. If such advice is ignored the Gunmaker may reasonably refuse to repair or work on a gun.

Principal reasons requiring Re-proof are:

1. Indication of weakness in action or barrel, including cracks or failure of the brazing of the lump. Severe pitting, bulges or dents.
2. Weakening, such as by conversion to ejector, repair of the action or barrel by gas welding.
3. Enlargement of the internal diameter of the barrel, e.g. to remove pitting or to lengthen the chamber, so that it no longer conforms with the existing Proof Marks.
4. Replacement of the action, barrel, barrel lump or extension.
5. Fitting of any attachment, such as a variable choke, which must withstand the pressure of firing.

Any gun proved for black powder should be re-proved if it is intended to be used with nitro smokeless powder cartridges.

Guns will not be accepted for Re-proof unless their condition complies with the requirements of Rules of Proof. It is preferable that they be submitted by a Gunmaker who knows the requirements and is able to do any preparatory work necessary. Guns are submitted at owner's risk of failure and the Gunmaker is entitled to payment for his services regardless of the result.

A gun which passes proof will be duly marked and may be used with confidence. In the event of rejection, if the fault can be corrected, the gun may be resubmitted. If finally rejected the Proof Authorities will deface the Proof Marks. The gun should then be rendered completely unserviceable to prevent its use by a person unaware of its unproved condition.

Under the Gun Barrel Proof Act 1868, it is an offence, subject to a penalty, to sell or offer for sale, exchange, pawn, or export a gun which does not bear valid Proof Marks.

Further information may be obtained from either Proof Masters at The Birmingham Proof House, Banbury Street, Birmingham B5 5RH, or The London Proof House, 48 Commercial Road, London E1 1LP.

CHAPTER TEN

Barrel Browning

I have always felt that the part of the Church of England marriage service that reminds us that marriage should 'not be lightly or wantonly undertaken' could equally have been written about barrel browning. This is not really remarkable, for both marriage and browning are long processes that require much patience and the prospect of both needs very careful thought and selection.

Naturally what should be rebrowned (and what should be left alone!) are questions on which diametrically opposed views are held. It is my opinion that original finish should not, under any circumstances, be removed if it can be avoided and that we should limit our efforts to those barrels to which, for reasons beyond our control, this has already happened.

So I have only experimented with guns on which the ribs had to be relaid, those that have had their damascus barrels incorrectly blued or, in one case, painted (an old wildfowling practice), and finally those on which previous clumsy attempts have resulted in what can only be described as a mess.

Like most surface finishes the final result depends greatly on the care that goes into preparation. A pair of barrels should be totally clean, smooth and polished but with all the sharp edges still sharp. For this reason I have always avoided using power tools which tend to round corners. Similarly, I always use very fine-grade emery paper to avoid deep scratches in the surface which must then be polished out again.

Depending on the condition of the barrels at the start their initial cleaning can represent a lot of work. Often there will be some rust stains that cannot be removed, without cutting very deep, and frankly I usually leave them, as we are often dealing with guns which already have very thin barrels.

The next stage is to 'degrease' the barrels and after this they must not be touched with the naked hands. There is sufficient grease transferred at each touch to spoil the final finish. So handles have to be provided and, at the same time, to prevent the browning solution attacking the bores, these handles take the form of plugs cut from a soft wood like pine. Corks can be used in some cases but before they are inserted it is wise to oil heavily or grease the insides of the barrels just in case the plugs leak and allow the browning solution to enter the bores.

It is generally agreed that solvents are not sufficient to remove the very last vestiges of grease and oil from the external barrel surfaces. I have tried many times without success.

1. The barrels are plugged with corks so that chalk can be used for degreasing.

Instead we have to revert to the traditional way, in which whiting or chalk, calcium carbonate from the chemist, has to be mixed with water to a slurry, the consistency of thin cream, this is then swabbed all over the barrels. When this has dried it is gently brushed off and the barrels are now degreased.

Now at last we are ready for the actual browning solution. There are scores, probably hundreds, of formulae for this job and many professionals have their own secret recipes. I chose the following formula for the ease with which its chemicals can be obtained – copper sulphate (2.8 g), solution of ferric chloride BPC (16.5 ml), concentrated nitric acid (2.8 ml), alcohol 90% (3.25 ml), and purified water to bring the solution up to 100 ml.

This in fact is a slight modification of the formula in Angier's *Firearm Blueing and Browning* on Page 83 No. C.10/k. The chief modification is to substitute the British Pharmaceutical Code strength of the ferric chloride solution which the enthusiast is most likely to be offered in place of the 29% solution mentioned by Angier. This is most unlikely to be available.

Having mentioned R. H. Angier's book I would most strongly urge anyone contemplating doing a lot of barrel browning to obtain a copy. As I have remarked before this book has been my 'bible' for more years than I care to count and I have never found it wanting.

The browning solution has to be lightly swabbed over the degreased barrels, and these are then set aside for at least 24 hours to rust. This coating has to be cleaned off with fine steel wool, when the barrels will look almost exactly as they did before the solution was applied. With repeated applications and removals the colour will start to develop. Then the rusting action has to be 'stopped' or neutralised by soaking the barrels in a warm alkali solution, about a tablespoonful of washing-soda or bicarbonate of soda in a pint of warm water. Beware! If the solution is boiling hot you can convert your browning into blueing! Finally the barrels have to be dried and oiled. A coat or two of wax polish and buffing with a soft duster will give pleasing depth as

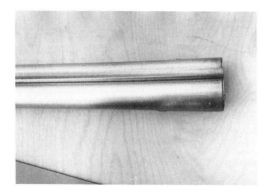

2. Once the barrels have been polished the hardest job is over.

an alternative final finish.

I have purposely made the last paragraph brief and a little vague because so many variables come into play. The rate or ease of browning depends on a host of factors, the most important being the type of damascus barrel, the temperature and humidity of the workshop and also the strength of the solution. But even this is an oversimplification because with barrel browning we are verging on a sort of 'black art'.

It is known that different people working in the same place with the same solutions produce differing results. Indeed it is further suggested that some members of a gunmaking family can brown to the highest standard while others can scarcely do so at all. Incidentally standing barrels in the corner of a nice warm kitchen is an ideal place for the rust to develop – which is another good reason for careful selection of both wife and gun barrels!

Barrel browning, while a seemingly simple process is, in fact, chemically very complex. Certainly iron, because of its atomic structure, can form a

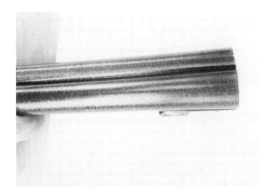

3. The reward – the figure of the barrels is brought out beautifully.

variety of oxides of varying colours and it is the proportion of these that produces the final colour.

It is relevant to mention that the so-called 'Plum Brown' solution which is sold under the 'Birchwood Casey' brand name is a totally different product and while I believe it produces an excellent brown colour, if the maker's instructions are followed, it will not bring out the figure of a damascus or twist barrel.

I can most usefully conclude with a few remarks on problems most likely to be encountered. The first is that if the solution only forms streaks or patches on the barrel it is not sufficiently degreased.

A problem that the amateur browner will encounter is that he needs small quantities of chemicals that have now virtually no use in day-to-day pharmacy. Some of them are also poisonous. Herein lies the heart of the problem. Perhaps the best answer to this is that the would-be browner seeks out an older-established pharmacy that is more likely to have the materials already in stock.

A customer seeking these relatively unusual items should choose a time when the shop is not busy, ask to speak to the pharmacist and leave a list of what is needed and be prepared to call back.

The items that are most likely to cause problems are ferric chloride solution and mercuric chloride found in many formulae. Since they pose different problems I will deal with them separately. Ferric chloride solution,

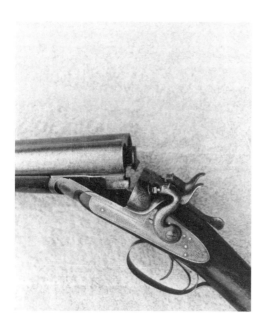

4.   A fine example of damascus barrel renovation – as near as possible to its original finish.

or as I first learned to call it 'Liq. Ferri Perchlor.', is still available; the smallest pack that can usually be bought from a wholesaler is 500 ml which will cost something like £2.00 retail.

If this material is not in stock in the pharmacy the only solution is to buy a whole bottle, since the proprietor of the pharmacy is unlikely to be prepared to buy a whole bottle in order to sell a small portion and be left with the greater part as an unsaleable residue. The problem is different in the case of mercuric chloride.

By law the purchaser must be either known to the pharmacist as a fit person to buy such a material or present a certificate signed either by a householder known to the pharmacist or by the police. The problem here is that if the pharmacy has no mercuric chloride in stock the smallest pack from the wholesaler is 25 g and it would be unwise for the amateur to buy and keep so much dangerous poison in his home. After all he will need only 2 or 3 g for 100 ml of browning solution which is far more than enough for a pair of barrels.

Because it seemed very likely that mercuric chloride would prove difficult, if not impossible, for many enthusiasts to obtain, I made up the formula as detailed earlier and this has certainly worked well. If at all possible use pure 90% alcohol, certainly not surgical spirit because this has a small oil content which we most definitely do not want.

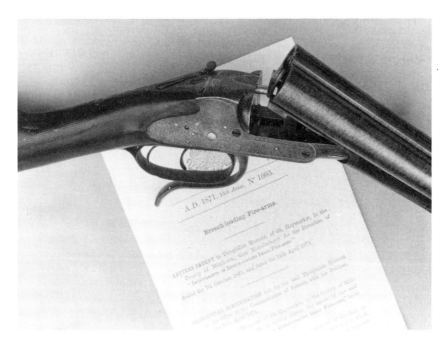

5.   Another restored gun – a Theophilus Murcott complete with its 1871 patent.

If after several applications the barrel still cleans back bright either there is a high proportion of steel in it, which has a greater resistance to corrosion, or you are working in too dry an atmosphere, such as a modern centrally heated home. In both instances a trick I have learned from a professional is to make a couple or so applications of a 2% solution of ammonium chloride (Sal Amoniac) – say about a level 5 ml spoonful in 100 ml of water. This will 'bite' into the barrel and seems to give the ordinary solution a start.

The most common problem is that the barrels are not uniformly coloured, which is the fault of the browner in that he hasn't applied his solution evenly or has not rubbed off the rust properly each time.

So much for what may be termed the basic outline of barrel browning. As in all trades there are tricks which some swear by and others will have nothing to do with. One tip worth trying is etching the barrels slightly with a strong solution of copper sulphate – care is needed not to let this go on too long since it can attack and disfigure the surface of the metal. Another more common ploy is to 'overbrown' the barrels, after which the colour can be lightened by gently rubbing down the surface with fine wire wool. This process can turn out very well – certainly I have had good results from it.

Ultimately, however, there is no substitute for experience. An awful lot can be learned with a pair of scrap barrels or with sections of discarded tubes from a barrel sleever. In this way an enthusiast will develop his own technique and come to know his materials. But all in all it is a lot of work, not to be lightly undertaken but, like marriage, wonderful when it works.

CHAPTER ELEVEN

The Blueing or Blacking of Gun Barrels

The title of this chapter indicates the first problem – what properly to call the process by which the bright silver colour of the raw steel barrels is transformed to a bluish-black tone. In general the gun trade refers to the colour as 'black' but in the case of older gun trade workers 'browning' is still occasionally used. The majority of shooters use the term 'blue' but for the purposes of this chapter I will use the modern trade term, i.e. 'black'.

Many of the remarks made in the previous chapter on browning will equally apply but some points will, nonetheless, bear repeating.

The origins of 'blacking' are rather obscure but there are two factors that may go some way towards explaining its beginnings. Firstly it is by no means easy to achieve an even brown colour on steel barrels. So when the steel barrel was first introduced, in the middle years of the last century, the old browning process, synonymous with damascus tubes, was found inadequate. However, for centuries steel, most notably pistol parts, has been 'blued' by a dry heating process that produces a bright, in some cases almost a hectic, blue colour. This latter bright blue was the result of heat blueing in a charcoal fire.

Against this background it is almost certain that the barrel browners already knew that if they overheated or steamed their work it would blacken. We will of course never know for certain, but it is a reasonable supposition that all these facts combined to produce the result we now know as blacking. The reason that these variations of colour are possible is because iron produces a complex set of coloured oxides whereas steel is purer and far less subject to variations.

In essence, therefore, we are seeking to form, on the surface of the barrel, a smooth, even, firmly adhering coloured oxide film. The principle being that once the surface has been subjected to 'controlled rusting' it will henceforth, to some degree, be immunised or protected from future rusting. To do this the surface of the barrel has to be carefully prepared. Any damage such as dents and bulges must be removed initially, because very little, if any, work can be done once the finish has been formed.

Next, the previous finish has to be completely removed and, because the sharp corners of the ribs and at the breech and muzzle ends of the barrels should be preserved, this means careful handwork with the finest grade of emery cloth. This will also avoid the possibility of deeply scoring or scratching the barrels, which would have to be subsequently removed by polishing. The exterior of the barrels can finally be wheel polished and must be so highly polished that they look as if they are chrome plated. This forms the foundation of the quality and appearance of the barrel finish.

The point to stress here is that a lot of work is involved to reach this stage; certainly it should be borne in mind when deciding whether to pay to have the job done by a professional or to undertake the work yourself.

Once the barrels are perfectly polished the next and absolutely essential stage is that the surfaces be degreased in just the same way as for browning. The best method, in my experience, is to coat the barrels with a slurry in water of whiting, chalk, calcium carbonate – call it what you will – it is all basically the same stuff. This slurry should be of a consistency of emulsion paint. It should be left to dry and then completely brushed off with a clean dry brush. Thereafter the surfaces must not be touched because human skin has a slightly greasy film which will quickly transfer to the surface of the steel.

With the preparation behind us, we now have to start the oxide-forming colouring process. Or in plain language – rust the exterior surface of the barrels. There are certainly scores and probably hundreds of formulae, some published and well known, some secret and credited with near-magical properties. There is no such thing as a 'best' formula, so much depends on the type and proportions of the chemicals and the technique of the user, and the environment in which he works. But what is sought is an even coating of fine rust.

The solution must be strong enough to 'bite' into the surface of the metal but it should not be so violent that it pits the tubes or causes coarse rust to form upon them.

In common with the advice given in the browning chapter, the amateur may find difficulty in obtaining some of the dangerous chemicals needed or indeed a pharmacist who can supply the relatively small quantities required to make up the solution.

One blacking solution which probably any chemist or chemistry lab. could easily make up consists of: nitric acid conc. 10 ml; copper sulphate 10 g; distilled water 40 ml. If you have no chemical background, let an expert make it up and remember that it is poisonous – so store it carefully. Another answer to the problem is to buy a ready-made solution from a specialist supplier.

Some say that the barrels should be oiled internally and plugged before they are degreased; others, including some of this country's leading specialists, say that this is unnecessary. However, if no plugs are used the chambers and bores must be carefully lapped out and polished otherwise internal rusting can occur in the future. Plugs in any event may admit liquid due to the expansion and contraction of the barrels during the process. If no plugs are used the barrels must only be touched on the lumps and by a hook inserted in the other end at the muzzles.

The rest of the process is quite simple – at least in theory. The barrels are swabbed with the rusting solution. At once it will be apparent if the degreasing was done properly. If the solution goes into streaks and blotches, then it wasn't and must be cleaned completely all over again. Assuming degreasing has been uniformly successful the barrels now have to be set aside to rust. How long depends on the temperature and humidity of the work place chosen but 24 hours is an average time. It is nearly impossible to obtain good results in a modern centrally heated house, with its very dry atmosphere. If you have a very tolerant wife, a kitchen is a useful environment due to its warmth, but failing this, the best warm, humid site will have to be sought. If all else fails, a sort of turkish bath in a tent might have to be constructed to reproduce the kind of warm humid conditions which are ideal.

When the rust has formed the barrels have to be immersed in a narrow metal trough of clean boiling water which is heated from beneath by a gas burner. They should be left in only long enough to heat the tubes thoroughly; two or three minutes should be adequate.

The barrels are next tipped towards the muzzles as these are taken out of the trough. Hold them vertically until they are completely drained and when they are dry, which will take only a minute or so due to heat evaporation, the rust is brushed off by hand with a very soft wire brush. If you have a very soft wire mechanical brush-machine this can be used.

This traditional 'slow rust' process must be repeated until a satisfactory depth of colour is obtained. How many 'passes' which are necessary to produce a good colour will depend on many factors such as the temperature, the strength of the solution and the rust resistance of the barrel steel. About six treatments is an average but it should be stressed that each 'pass' or treatment should be thoroughly completed and that the metal will rust less and less after each successive swabbing with solution.

Having finally produced the required depth of colour you will want to preserve it and prevent further rusting. Some blueing formulae seem to be rather prone to a phenomenon known as 'after rusting' in which, despite oiling, rust spots seem to emerge from the metal itself beneath the oil film. This 'after rusting' troubles even professional barrel blackers from time to time and is often a symptom of the mixing of the formulae going wrong either by incorrect measures or even a change of brand of one of the chemical constituents. It is also often caused by small residual traces of the blueing solution still lying on the surface of the barrels and, since this solution is an acid, it must be neutralised by making the water for the last immersion strongly alkaline. A spoonful of bicarbonate of soda stirred into the last trough of clean boiling water is all that is needed.

All that remains is for the blacking to be removed from those areas where it is undesirable i.e. the muzzle and breech faces and the barrel lumps and flats. This is done by wrapping fine emery cloth around a flat square block of wood and stroking in one direction until the blacking disappears and silver remains. The barrels then need to be waxed, to fill the pores of the metal, and finally polished with a clean soft duster.

These are the basics of barrel blacking, but what no book or article can teach is skill and judgement (of how much and how long?), that only comes with practice! As in the browning chapter, I would urge any tyro barrel blacker to try his hand first on a scrap pair of barrels or cut-off tubes from a sleever before he embarks on the attempt to black the barrels of his best gun. Finally, the whole process is very time consuming and certainly is not to be done only on a wet Sunday afternoon when there happens to be nothing on TV. But if you have the time to spare and the right temperament and chemicals to hand it can be very satisfying indeed – not to mention the amount of money which is saved.

CHAPTER TWELVE

Jointing

How often have we heard shooting people discuss the qualities and virtues of jointing? Yet in terms of technical knowledge, very little is known, outside the gun trade, about the skills that go into 'jointing' guns.

It is generally accepted that this is the most skilful operation to perform in the manufacture of a shotgun – the fitting of the barrels to the action. It is often said that the life of any gun is only as good as its jointing and, true or false, it is certainly a very important factor when considering the purchase of a shotgun.

Consider for a moment the skill involved in effecting an as near perfect fit between barrels and action. This requires many years of training, the complete mastery of one's tools, total concentration and the gift of being able to use one's hands to perform tasks with basic hand tools that few are ever capable of achieving. These attributes are only acquired after years of experience. It is no wonder that the majority of English guns last more than a lifetime.

We have all seen examples of guns that are loose or have what is commonly known as 'a headache'. In some cases they are neither old nor well worn but have seen only a few seasons. One cause is heavy load cartridges in light game guns. Another common problem area is the cross-pin – the hook of the front lump becomes worn resulting in it becoming oversized. However the commonest causes are poorly finished working surfaces and the use of metal which is too soft. The majority of English guns are an excellent example of the skill required, for seldom do they need the attention of a gunmaker because of looseness.

Certain special tools are required. Usually these are made in the formative years of a gun worker's apprenticeship and are an exact copy of the masters. In some cases they have been handed down from father to son. Many of my own tools, which I still use today, are over a hundred years old.

Every time a cartridge is fired from your gun the action tends to move backwards and the barrels forwards, and certain fundamentals have to be observed in an endeavour to keep the action face on the barrels. The cross-pin must fit tight around the hook, at the same time the circle of the rear lump (or steel) must fit exactly when the action closes. It goes without saying that the steels of the barrels fit correctly into the slots of the action. A similar principle of jointing is used for boxlocks, sidelocks and over-and-unders.

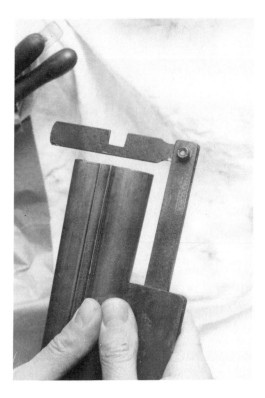

1.   The barrel square is made by the gunmaker himself usually during his apprenticeship period. The breech face of the barrels is squared from both sides including the flats. Note the portion cut out on the blade; when turned around it allows for barrels that have top rib extensions.

Best-quality English guns are renowned throughout the world for the smoothness and ease with which they open and close. It has often been said, and I am sure demonstrated by many persons experienced in the handling of fine sporting guns, that if blindfolded and placed in front of a varied selection of shotguns that by opening and closing each gun, together with the feel, they would be able to tell if they were English or foreign. This feel, the ease with which the gun opens and the smoothness in its closing, is a result of many different parts being filed and fitted with a delicacy of touch.

Starting with the rough action forging, the first stage in the jointing process is the preparation of the slots. Both must be roughed out by machine and then hand filed perfectly flat and square. The rear slot must naturally be in line with the front one. Having filed both slots out to size, the smoothest of hand files is used to achieve a mirror-like surface. The knuckle must also be square to the cross-pin hole of the action and again smoothed and polished so that all scratches and file marks are removed.

The final operation is to smooth the flats and face of the action, not forgetting to leave a small radius where both meet to give the corner strength and, at the same time, accommodate the radius on the edge of the barrel flats. For the time being the action can be placed on one side whilst the preparation of the barrels commences.

The lumps have to be machined and filed flat, perfectly square and above all in the exact centre of the tubes. Not only are the lumps square with the breech face of the barrels they are also square with the flats. It is absolutely essential, when jointing the two together, to make sure that both the lumps and slots are smooth, clean and lightly lubricated with a thin film of oil or grease. This is to prevent what are called 'runners', that is minute pieces of steel filings or grit, coming between the two surfaces and scoring them.

Smoke black is used to detect where the high spots are. This involves using a lamp made from a small empty bottle or tin with a pierced screw cap through which passes a wick which soaks up paraffin from inside the bottle.

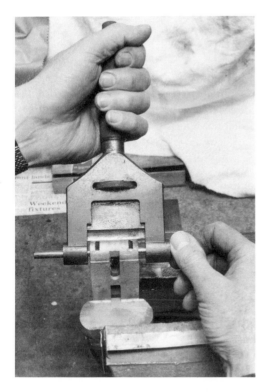

2.   The knuckle of the action has to be scraped so that it is perfectly square with the cross-pin hole and, at the same time, it should be smooth and highly polished.

When lit it produces thin black smoke which deposits soot on surfaces the flame is held against.

The action is closed onto the barrels by hand and gently squeezed in the vice – the emphasis being on the gently. Both vice guards and a special guard for protection of the barrels are used. Having removed the action from the barrels it can now be clearly seen where the high spots are. These are betrayed by silver patches where the 'smoke black' (soot) have been removed by contact and pressure. It is then a case of gradually removing these high bearing surfaces with a dead smooth file and repeating the operation until finally the action goes fully home and no silver patches remain thus proving a perfectly flat pair of surfaces.

Another method of assessing whether or not the lumps fit correctly is to push the action upside down onto the back lump of the barrels – it should stay on of its own accord. During the jointing we must not forget the circle, a most important part of the lumps which helps to pull the action down onto the face of the barrels. When this stage is reached both the flats of the barrels and those of the action should just be touching. A line is then scribed through the cross-pin hole onto the front lump to enable the rough shape of the hook to be filed out.

Once completed, both barrels and action are joined together and a cutter is put down the cross-pin hole. This ensures that both the hook and the cross-pin hole of the action are perfectly in line. The action is removed once again, all the sharp edges, machining marks and burrs are removed. A fine-grade oval file is then used to smooth and polish the hook.

The cross-pin can now be fitted, a very exacting job and one that cannot be rushed. It cannot be overstressed that both the hook and the pin must be kept spotlessly clean during the fitting operation. All the high spots must be removed to acquire an even, flat bearing surface at both the top and bottom of the hook. A method used in trying the fit of both is to remove the cross-pin, push it into the hook holding it with the thumb and then try and move it from

3.   A variety of tools the jointer needs in order to carry out the near-perfect fit of action to barrels.

side to side to detect 'play' or sideways movement with the other hand.

Finally comes the fitting of the fore-end iron. This again has to fit the knuckle of the action perfectly and lies centrally on the loop for, when the iron is fitted to the barrels, it must help push the cross-pin up into the hook and keep it there.

Apart from 'blacking down' to obtain the final fit of the face of the barrels in relation to the face of the action, the gun has been jointed. Now comes the moment of truth and a check on the quality of jointing.

Remember that the gun has to open and close with ease and at the same time be a perfect fit. A simple test is to insert a piece of cigarette paper between the circle of the barrels and the action – you should not be able to close the gun. Place another piece of paper between the face of the action and the breech face of the barrels – again the gun should not close. If we consider the number of bearing surfaces there are on a conventional side-by-side gun, that have to operate all at the same time, it is no wonder that jointing is possibly *the* most exacting skill of the gunmaker's art.

This skill is taken to extreme limits on guns with extra sets of barrels. In

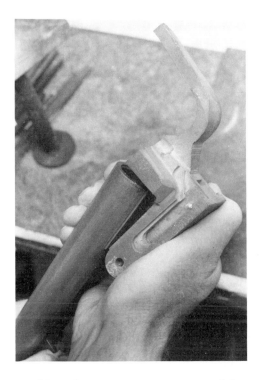

4. Note the top strap bent up out of the way. This is to allow the bolt hole to be filed flat and square. The action is pushed onto the barrel lumps by hand taking great care that no excessive force is applied.

the days when I served my apprenticeship many customers had sets of three guns (trios) made, all with interchangeable barrels that would fit any one of the three guns.

In producing guns of this quality another important factor has to be considered – the striker hole. The firing pin must strike exactly in the centre of the cartridge primer every time.

Solid cross-pins and various types of over-and-under guns present other, quite different problems. Much of the work involved on guns in the cheaper range is carried out by machine but to fairly close tolerances, thus reducing the amount of costly handworking skills. It must be stressed that if your gun is showing any signs of looseness then it can only get worse if neglected and the gun should be taken to a practical gunsmith, preferably one who knows about jointing, as soon as possible to rectify the cause.

In my experience it is not the policy of the reputable professionals in the gun trade to build up the hook or lumps by means of welding or metal spraying.

CHAPTER THIRTEEN

Barrel Sleeving

Anyone owning a gun which has barrels that are thin with wear and nearing the end of their life, is faced with one of two options. He can either have new barrels fitted or have the old barrels sleeved.

Explained simply, sleeving is a process whereby the old barrels are cut off in front of the chambers, and replaced by new tubes which are close fitted and 'sweated' (soldered) into the remaining barrel stumps which have been precision bored to receive them.

This may sound a crude process but executed by a skilled craftsman it is a time-proved alternative to the expense of a completely new set of barrels. It also offers a considerable saving. Sleeved barrels usually cost approximately one third of the expense of fitting completely new ones. The main saving is made by the entire breech ends and the lumps etc. already being present, so far less work is required.

However there are some who will not consider sleeving at any price. In this case the only other options are to have new barrels fitted, regardless of the cost, or relegate that old faithful companion to a permanent place in the gun cabinet or rack simply to be admired from time to time.

Through former neglect or even accident, many guns arrive at a stage where this decision has to be made. The stock, action and fore-end of the gun may be near perfect, but the cost of fitting a set of new barrels can be disproportionate to the resale value of the gun. Nonetheless it makes little sense to discard what is potentially a very sound weapon and the financial consideration may not be the only criterion.

Craftsman-built new barrels seldom come cheap. A large proportion of the cost is involved in jointing the barrels to the action. The gunmaker's skills are thoroughly put to the test in this operation and no mistakes can be made.

If top rib extensions, such as a crossbolt or 'doll's head', are incorporated then the task is even more exacting – not to mention time consuming. A plain double underbite, where no extension to the top rib is employed, is a much less demanding proposition.

As mentioned earlier the strikers (firing pins) must line up exactly with the centre of the bore. The rear end of the top rib must be perfectly in line with the shield on top of the action breech and the width of the barrels must of course match the width of the standing breech of the action. The fore-end will of course have to be refitted and the ejector work coupled up. These are all tasks which are far too difficult for most shooting men even to contemplate.

Sleeving avoids most of these costly procedures by utilising the breech ends of the barrels complete and the extra cost of jointing new barrels to the action simply does not arise. Despite this, even sleeving, being a precision engineering exercise, is far beyond the layman's capability.

However a large proportion of sleeved barrels usually need minor re-jointing which is normally considered a part of the job. When cut off, the barrel stumps have to be precision machine bored in readiness to receive new barrel tubes – as with new barrels these have to be chambered. New ribs will have to be shaped, filed and laid.

There is one notable advantage to either sleeving or new barrels in that prior to the work being carried out you can of course specify the length of barrel, the chokes required and in some cases a modern chambering. Having done this your barrels are filed, 'struck-up' and polished ready for blacking. Your gun can now be put back into service and is ready for another lifetime's shooting.

There is a widespread belief that sleeving diminishes the value of the gun. Some of the reasons given for this are worth comment, especially those which cast doubts since 'sleeving' is comparatively new to the English gun trade. It can be said that both London and Birmingham proof houses have passed many thousands of sleeved guns over many years and there can no longer be any doubt that this kind of barrel replacement, if carried out by an expert, is as perfectly safe as a gun with original barrels. However there is equally no doubt that a high quality gun, be it sidelock or boxlock, is worth more with first class original or new barrels than with sleeved barrels.

The economics of sleeving

Many factors have to be considered before a final decision is made. It is always a good idea to consult a practical gunsmith who has had experience of this type of work and is prepared to discuss your thoughts with you. But as a 'rule of thumb' guide the following suggestions may be of some help:

1. The cheaper makes of gun should always be sleeved, unless the gun is still in mass production and new barrels are available. The cost of new hand-made barrels would normally far exceed the value of the gun.

2. Medium-quality guns need more consideration. A non-ejector gun is usually less valuable than an ejector model. The maker's name on the rib will often indicate, to some extent, the original quality. The better-quality gun should always be considered for rebarrelling. The resale value must be calculated due to the gun inevitably being more valuable with new barrels fitted, although whether one could recover even the cost of new barrels if the gun were sold, is a problem facing many.

3. 'Best' guns i.e. sidelocks or boxlock ejectors of high quality should ideally be fitted with new barrels. This work should be undertaken by the original makers every time, if they are still in business. Often one sees new

barrels of poor quality fitted to high-quality guns with a virtually unknown or second-rank maker's name on the rib. This practice can adversely influence the value of the gun if you contemplate selling or even retaining it as an investment.

Quality of work

Who will be doing the job? Give it some careful thought – the cheapest job often turns out to be the most expensive in the long run. A common result, with many guns that have been sleeved, is the apparent lack of balance or at least a distinct change in the 'feel' of the gun in the hands. This is often due to either a lack of quality in the workmanship, or the old barrels having lost a significant amount of metal over the years from dent repairs or corrosion, wear and tear. The thickness of the new tubes is down to the judgement of the barrel filer concerned.

If balance and handling qualities are an important consideration always be prepared to have the gun rebalanced too. This means adding weight to the interior of the butt to counterbalance the extra weight in the forward part of the barrels. The handling qualities will be retained but the extra weight is a largely inescapable fact of life. These remarks apply particularly to entirely new barrels and to a lesser extent to those which are sleeved.

Striking up of the tubes is most important especially where they have been sleeved. Are the ribs straight and nicely shaped to follow the contours of the tubes? Is the fore-end loop fitted onto the tubes so that the fore-end itself lines up exactly with the knuckle of the action? The barrels should be struck up and shaped so that the grooves in the fore-end wood fit perfectly on the tubes.

It is always worth asking to see a similar example of the gunsmith's work before giving him your order. Most reputable gunsmiths will be only too pleased to show you the quality of their work. You will then know what to expect and can be quoted a price. Very similar questions can be asked about new barrels but the decision is still yours: New barrels or sleeved, to return your gun to its former condition?

CHAPTER FOURTEEN

General Care and Storage

Proper cleaning of a gun will extend its lifetime and improve its appearance as well as help to maintain its safety and value. Some guns may need more frequent thorough cleanings than others; this depends obviously on how often they are used and the climate they are used in. All guns should be cleaned immediately after use and inspected frequently, particularly before the start of a new season.

Cleaning the barrels

The method of cleaning the bores of the barrels varies quite a lot but the basic intention is the same – to remove all moisture, fouling and deposits to prevent any unwanted corrosion taking place. What follows is one method among many.

Firstly, with just the cleaning rod, push balls of paper (kitchen roll is ideal) down each barrel from the chamber end. This will remove moisture, excessive powder residue and soiling.

Next attach the phosphor bronze bristle brush to the cleaning rod and pass this up and down the bores two or three times to remove any further powder fouling. Again push clean balls of paper down the bore and look carefully to see if much fouling persists.

Carefully examine the 'lead-in' from the chamber to the bore and behind the chokes for smears of lead left adhering to the barrel walls. If this is excessive it is likely that the lead shot in the cartridges used is soft or 'unchilled'. The use of cartridges loaded with wads which employ a plastic sleeve e.g. 'Plaswads' has largely eliminated leading as well as some 'shot deformation'.

If 'leading' is present swab the bore with a clean patch soaked in one of the spirit solvents especially made for the purpose. Give this a few minutes to dissolve or dislodge the leading and then clean out with a brush followed by a clean patch.

Finally look through the bore to check that all fouling and leading has gone. If it has, a polish with a clean lamb's wool mop followed by a light film of oil from another lamb's wool mop is all that is needed.

It is worth noting that all cleaning patches should be discarded rather than re-used continually since the risk of particles of grit being re-introduced into the barrels must be avoided. Also, try to keep one lamb's wool mop for polishing and another for oiling and periodically rinse that one out in warm soapy water to cleanse of old tacky oil.

Always dry out the bores before firing the gun since excessive oil can itself become an obstruction and risk causing either a bulge, rivelling or even a burst barrel.

The extractors and their holes are a trap for moisture and dirt so periodically clean them and their holes using a feather. Once you are sure they are clean, smear on a light film of oil and slip them back into place. Replace the extractor retaining pin, but clean the pin and the hole first. The extractors need not be removed every time you clean your gun after shooting, but they should be taken out if the gun has been used in heavy rain.

The final task on the barrels is the outside, with particular attention being paid to the ribs where they join the barrels and where water and dirt often collect. Having made sure they are clean, wipe over with an oily rag.

A very important point to remember is that blood and salt water can be prime causes of rusting on barrels – if either of these come into contact with the metal, try to clean as soon as possible to avoid the possibility of rust and the loss of some barrel blueing. Also keep an eye on the gun for some days after since salt, if left unchecked, will cause rusting and the oil will *not* prevent it!

The action

This part of the gun is far more difficult to clean and some shooters believe that the more oil they put into slots and holes, the more it will prevent rusting and corrosion and so ensure a better service to their gun. This is not so! The head of the stock and parts of the fore-end wood will not absorb cleaning oil well, as they will linseed oil, and, in time, the wood will become spongy and ultimately rot.

Wipe the external metal areas with a light film of oil – this includes the triggers, trigger guard, top lever, safety thumbpiece, the entire action body including the flats and face but at all times be sparing so that you can pick up the gun without your hands becoming oily.

Clean those inaccessible places by means of a feather such as the striker holes, and slots and cams on the fore-end. Start by using a clean dry feather and later apply a little oil to the feather and repeat the operation.

If you are out shooting in heavy rain or do a lot of wildfowling, water may penetrate the action of your gun and it can then, if neglected, rust internally and cause many problems possibly resulting in costly repairs.

A minor adjustment or an early repair can often save embarrassment in the shooting field and even prevent the loss of several days' shooting at the busiest time of the season.

The woodwork

Your gun's stock will have been given one of several types of finish that are on the market. Among the most popular is French (or button) polish or the conventional 'English' oil-finished stock that has been polished by hand.

After a day's shooting in the rain many shooting men palm a few drops of linseed oil into their stock. In the case of an 'English' oil-finished stock, simply rub the stock well afterwards with the palm of your hand. This will help to bring back its life and beauty.

Stocks that have been given one of the many types of sealed finish are simply wiped over with a dry clean cloth, since linseed oil will not penetrate a sealed or varnish finish. The chequering is cleaned with the aid of a soft bristle nail brush, but not one with plastic bristles. Gently brush backwards and forwards working down the lines in the chequering.

Storage

Having completed the cleaning of the gun, we now have to decide where to store it. Many problems can result from guns being stored in wet or damp cases and damp rooms.

If storing only until the following day, make sure that before laying it away into its case, the gun and the case itself are quite dry. This particularly applies if storing in a gun slip. If the gun is being stored for long periods of time, ensure that you inspect it on a regular basis. It is not sufficient to lift the lid of the case and look inside – lift the gun out of its case and thoroughly inspect it, also check the case.

The reason for this regular attention is that many of the materials used to line the compartments of gun cases, for example baize or felt, will themselves absorb moisture from a humid atmosphere. In time this will transfer to the gun and eventually cause, sometimes heavy, pitting at the points of contact.

It is, in many respects, wiser to stand the gun in a rack in a well-ventilated room and use the case only for travelling (as it was intended).

Gun security

Each year many guns are stolen from ordinary private houses often during the course of the ever growing number of casual 'break ins' and burglaries. At the time of writing we are being threatened with statutory security controls, which should be stoutly resisted by the shooting community, but in any event, it is the moral responsibility of every shooting man to consider the safe storage and security of his guns, if only from the point of view of preventing the loss of a valuable and treasured possession.

Many shooting men have wisely chosen to purchase a steel gun cabinet. These are normally made of at least 14 SWG steel plate with edges that are usually folded for extra strength. On most models the door is inset, and the

189

hinges are concealed to prevent unscrewing them. Among other features included are the fitting with two Chubb five-lever anti-theft locks. Many varying types are available.

Security cabinets can be purchased to store up to fifteen guns and some are encased inside a hardwood cabinet when they make very attractive pieces of furniture. The siting of your cabinet needs to be considered very carefully, perhaps in the cupboard under the stairs with another security lock on the

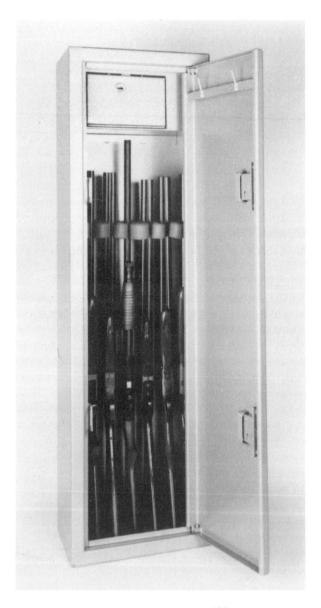

cupboard door or in the garage, especially if it is built onto the house: maybe the spare bedroom? The choice is yours.

The majority of cabinets are made to bolt to the wall and some are fixed up off the floor. Don't put your guns away after the season ends and forget to look at them until your first shooting date, although most shooters nowadays shoot at some time in the close season. Make sure you carry out regular inspections and if any work needs to be carried out give your gunsmith ample time to execute the work required – he will usually be busiest just before the season opens – as this will save disappointment in not having your gun returned in time.

Insurance

It is surprising how many people there are whose guns are insufficiently covered by insurance. They either fail to take the trouble to read the small print on the policy, or simply undervalue the guns in their possession. Remember you will need to insure for the full replacement value, which may well, over the years, be substantially more than the figure you paid. With a good-quality English gun and some high-grade imported guns remember to increase the insured value as the years go by. In the case of a modern gun this is easy since its value is given by a current price list.

With older guns it is quite a different matter and unless you bought the gun recently and have a proper bill to show the insurance people you will need to get a professional valuation or appraisal. Make sure you go to someone who knows what he is doing and is qualified by experience to value your gun. Also use someone who can give you a written valuation for insurance purposes. If you trust your local gunsmith and you make regular purchases from him he may give you a written valuation without charge as a favour. But an unknown gunsmith may make a token charge which is often based on a small percentage of the estimated value of the gun. Due to the small difference in premium it is well worth insuring for the maximum value since in the event of a claim for damage (or indeed total loss by theft or fire) you will not regret it.

Membership of the BASC (The British Association for Shooting and Conservation) and other shooting organisations includes shooting insurance cover but always check exactly what that cover is since only third-party claims are usually covered. But, if you wish to arrange your own insurance choose a good company who offer good cover at a reasonable cost but do not be tempted to pay too little, since there is no such thing as cheap insurance.

Finally remember to write down details of your gun in case of loss. This should include the serial number, the maker and his address and the model with any distinguishing features which might help trace the gun if it were lost or stolen. A set of photographs is also a good idea.

CHAPTER FIFTEEN

Glossary

Gunmaking has a language of its own and I am the first to admit that I am not generally conscious of using it but you will often find that most gun trade workers are much the same.

So perhaps the following glossary will be of help to those wishing to understand the sometimes strange terms used and their meanings, and who aspire to become fluent in gunmaking terminology. There may be many terms, phrases and names with which you are already familiar but you may none the less find the following list useful.

Bore size   The method of indicating the size of a shotgun is very old and dates back to the time of muzzle-loading cannon. A cannon which fired a solid round shot (cannonball) of 12 pounds in weight was described as a 'Twelve Pounder', and so on for other sizes. This old system of gauging has survived for shotguns.

A '12 bore' shotgun is of such a size that 12 perfectly spherical balls of solid lead, and of the same diameter as the bore, would weigh exactly one pound. Similarly if the bore took one of 20 balls of lead whose total weight was one pound then the gun would be a 20 bore. The expression '12 gauge' is used in North America as well as here in Great Britain and means the same thing.

Therefore in gunmaking we have the unusual system of classification whereby the smaller the number, the larger the bore. There are a few exceptions to this rule – for example the .410 and 9mm garden guns, both of which are classified in the same way as rifles, i.e. the actual diameter of the bore in fractions of an inch or millimetres. However, in reality modern guns are made to specific decimal or metric measurements. No one uses balls of lead to determine the bore any more but, quaintly, the term persists in use.

The full range of shotgun bores in current, common use includes 4, 8, 10, 12, 16, 20 and 28 bore, and .410 and 9mm etc.

The 12 bore is of course by far the most popular and recognised as the standard size in Great Britain and North America.

Tubes   This is the term which is normally used to describe barrels when they are actually being made, due obviously to their tubular shape. But the term is also carried over so that if you were to take your gun into a gunsmith in order that he remove a dent from the barrel, he might refer to it as a dent in the tube which, in the strictest terms, it is, if you think about it!

Breech   The end of the barrels into which the cartridges will be loaded –
it is from this point that all measurements are taken in relation to the making
of a pair of barrels. Also a term describing the entire action and rear end of
the barrels when they are fitted together.

Chamber(s)   This is the part of the barrel at the breech end which is wider
than the bore and which accepts the cartridge. It will be of a diameter and
depth to receive, according to the size and proof specification given, and in
12 bore this can be 2", 2$\frac{1}{2}$", 2$\frac{3}{4}$" or 3" cartridges. The most popular sizes are
2$\frac{1}{2}$" or 2$\frac{3}{4}$". In former times the cartridge case length was given as the size
but nowadays the deciding factor is proofing, i.e. a 2$\frac{3}{4}$" chamber gun will
normally have been proofed at 3$\frac{1}{4}$ tons per square inch. Each case length has
its corresponding service and proof pressure.

It should be carefully noted that while a 12 bore gun with a 3" chamber
(often referred to as a magnum) can accommodate a shorter cartridge length
no attempt should ever be made to fire a longer cartridge than denoted. For
instance, a 2$\frac{3}{4}$" cartridge in a 2$\frac{1}{2}$" chambered and proofed gun is potentially
dangerous not because the cartridge will not fit but because of the higher
pressure of the 2$\frac{3}{4}$" cartridge. This might seem to be merely stating the
obvious, but if you have changed guns and have a mixture of cartridges you
should be extremely careful. Never mix different bore size cartridges in bag
or pocket.

Extractors   As the gun is opened this part rises from below and between
the chambers of most 'break action' shotguns. Its purpose is to lift empty or
unfired cartridges from the chambers so that they can be grasped and
removed. With over-and-under guns the extractors may be positioned
differently.

Ejectors   This is superficially the same part as the 'extractor' except that,
in double-barrel 'ejector' guns, the part is split into two halves which work
side by side. They throw fired cartridge cases clear of the chambers. If only
one barrel is fired only that barrel's ejector operates. Should both barrels be
fired both ejectors work in unison. Conversely if neither barrel is fired and
the gun is opened the ejectors function only as extractors.

In the case of over-and-under shotguns the ejectors are often fitted on each
side of the chambers rather than beneath but positions vary according to
make and design.

The force, which enables the ejector to throw the empty case clear of the
chamber, is obtained by the 'kicker' striking the base of the ejector leg. Its
power usually comes from coil or leaf springs attached to the fore-end iron
and housed in a recess in the fore-end wood.

In many inexpensive single-barrelled shotguns the similar ejector throws
out both fired and unfired cartridges indiscriminately. These guns are often
described as 'automatic' ejector guns – a somewhat misleading term since
unless the chamber is blocked by the palm of the hand, and the cartridge
trapped, it will be dumped on the ground.

Extractor bed or 'way'   This is the part in which the extractors or ejectors fit.

Extractor pin   Keeps the extractor (or ejectors) in place and governs their length of movement.

Barrel face   The external flat area of the breech end of the barrels – the part which fits flush with the face of the action when the gun is closed.

Rim recesses   The recess cut into the outer edge of the chambers to accommodate the rim at the head of the cartridge. This allows the cartridge to be either lifted out or ejected.

Head space   This is the distance the heads of the cartridges are from the face of the action when lying in the chambers with the gun closed. Obviously this is controlled by the depth of the chamber rims. This clearance is necessary to allow the gun to close without the bases of the cartridges contacting the breech face. Conversely if the rim recesses are excessively deep and the cartridges therefore have a lot of backward and forward play the recoil or 'kick' of the gun can be increased noticeably. Normal (or indeed excessive) head space can be heard, when the gun is tipped forward and backward, as slight clicks as the cartridges slide in the chambers.

Guns of 'Monobloc' (sliding breech) construction, such as the French Darne action, have virtually no 'head space' and as a result recoil (or kick) less than conventional break action guns which require head space to function safely.

Barrel flats   This is a term normally applied only to side-by-side guns. It is the flat area under the breech end of the barrels, which fits flush on the action flats, and on which most of the proof marks are stamped.

Proof marks   These are letters, figures and symbols punched into the barrel and action flats to indicate the gauge, length of chamber, service pressure tested at, black powder or nitro proof and whether proofed in London or Birmingham or indeed a foreign country. These will also often indicate the nominal bore diameter at 9″ from the breech end shown in decimals, e.g. .729″ for 12 bore. But bear in mind that proof marks changed in line with rules of 1909, 1925 and 1954. So older guns may carry variations in markings such as the nominal bore diameter being shown in fractions, instead of decimals. See Chapter 9.

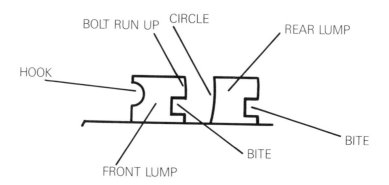

Barrel lumps   Also referred to as the 'steels'. These are the two pieces (sometimes only one piece) of metal which protrude from the underside of the breech end of the barrels in order to act as a pivot point and to fit into the action to enable the gun to be locked shut.

Hook   The part of the lump which enables the barrel to rotate open while in position on the action. In the case of a side-by-side this will invariably be on the front lump.

On over-and-unders the positioning of the lumps varies according to the design of the gun and the depth of the action body – but the same principles apply and the lumps are immediately obvious to the eye.

Bites   An area cut out of the back of each lump on a side-by-side to allow the bolt of the action to slide into them and lock the action shut. The method of the 'bite' or locking system varies on some side-by-sides and many over-and-unders. For example with modern over-under Winchester and Miroku guns there is a full-width bite of the bottom barrel. Beretta feature two recesses (at either side of the barrel face) which accommodate two rods which protrude from the action when closed.

Circle   On the side-by-side you find the circle is a curved surface on the front of the back lump – its function is to pull the barrels tight onto the action. On over-and-unders you will find that its position will vary.

Top extension   A third bite, occasionally associated with 'magnum' guns, will sometimes be found protruding from between the barrels at the breech end as an extension to the top rib. This fits into a slot in the top of the action between the breech faces. This extra bite supplements the main bites in the lumps although in some cases replaces one of the two main bites. These top rib extensions take many forms such as 'stepped' or 'doll's head' or round or square crossbolts. All serve the same purpose.

Chopper & dovetail   These relate to the lumps. Some side-by-sides have dovetailed lumps; these are made separately and are brazed between the underside of the two tubes. 'Best' and some imported guns often feature 'chopper' lumps which are part of the original barrel forging and become an integral part of each of the two tubes. Whilst chopper lump barrels are undoubtedly stronger this does not imply that dovetailed lumps are in any way weaker since it is rare for dovetailed lumps to fail. The expression 'chopper' lump is derived from the appearance of each single unassembled barrel looking rather like a crude axe or 'chopper'.

Monobloc   Monobloc construction is a relatively recent innovation which simplifies barrel building. The entire breech is made from a single block of metal which has the contours of the barrels, the rear end of the top rib, the lumps and the extractor way all machined from this single piece of steel.

Very accurate diameters are bored through the block to accept the tubes which are then 'sweated' and soldered into place. Conventional ribs are then laid.

In broad terms this resembles the more recent practice of 'sleeving' new tubes into the original breech thus saving the extensive cost of entirely new barrels.

The most notable use of 'monobloc' construction was on the precision-engineered, high-quality guns by Darne and Charlin of France which employed a non-breaking action and a sliding breech block locking system. The design, though exceptionally well made and fast handling, proved too radical a change for the shooting population of Britain to take to.

Loop   Again to be found on the underside of the barrels, in front of the lumps – its purpose is to attach the fore-end.

Keel piece   Also known as the butt piece, it is a short piece of bottom rib which runs from the beginning of the flats to the fore-end loop which is occasionally integral.

Ribs   There are two ribs, top and bottom, which are simply shaped strips of metal that join the barrels for their full length – on top and underneath (in the case of a side-by-side). They will add some strength to the joining of the barrels but their principal function is as a sighting plane and being aesthetically pleasing to the eye and as such can vary in shape, width, height and method of finish.

In side-by-sides the choice is between a conventional concave top rib (commonly known as a 'game' rib), flat rib or 'Churchill'. This latter rib is similar to a flat rib but is tapered to a flat-topped pyramid and slightly raised for the whole of its length. It also tapers towards the muzzle end of the barrels.

Ribs can show even greater variation on over-and-unders from narrow to broad and high-stepped ribs on trap guns. The finish of the top surface of the rib also comes in various forms from smooth through 'matted' ribs to file-cut (a similar finish to that of a single cut file blade), cross-milling, and longitudinal wavy lines called 'engine turning'.

Over the years there have been a few guns made which lack normal ribs and whose barrels are only joined at the breech with a short rib which dips downwards. There is naturally a short connector at the muzzles and half way down the barrels. John Dickson of Edinburgh made some guns in this way and several modern over-and-unders have a similar lack of connecting ribs.

There is of course no bottom rib on an over-and-under, but a middle rib instead which occasionally has equidistant cooling ports cut through it.

Ventilated top ribs   These top ribs are also 'ventilated' or slotted through the side of the rib for most of its length. They tend to stand higher than normal off the barrels to which they are attached. Some are constructed from small sections giving the appearance of a series of small bridges. Their intention is to help to overcome 'heat shimmer' which is a disruption of the sight when heatwaves rise from an extremely hot barrel. It can be compared to a desert mirage in some ways. This can only be really useful after many cartridges are fired in fairly quick succession therefore the ventilated rib is usually only fitted to guns intended for clay pigeon competitions. For ordinary field shooting these attractive ribs provide an ideal home for dirt.

Nose ends   These are roughly triangular plugs of steel which are soldered between where the barrels meet at the muzzle and the top and bottom ribs.

Muzzle   The opposite end to the breech, where barrels come together and the shot leaves the barrel.

Sights   The foresight is usually a bead type sight positioned just short of the muzzles and made of either brass, silver or ivory and threaded into the top rib. The modern 'tunnel' sight in red or white nylon is an elongated version of the bead. Some guns also have a small bead sight positioned half way down the top rib. This is often called a 'trap' sight, having at one time been popular with 'Olympic trap' competitors.

Internal finish   This relates to the insides or bores of the barrels which can be finished in one of two ways. The bores of traditional guns are chemically untreated being steel all through; other than that they are very highly polished to achieve a mirror-smooth finish. Some modern guns however feature a chrome-plated finish. These plated-bore barrels almost entirely eliminate the need to clean the bores but have a serious disadvantage. Should the barrels be dented or the chokes need to be altered the chrome plating must be chemically stripped i.e. removed, the repairs or alterations carried out and the bores replated. Naturally the bores beneath the plating are not as well polished as a conventional barrel.

Chokes   This is a constriction of the bore at the muzzle end to concentrate the density of the shot pattern thrown by the barrel. It has a gradual taper or 'cone' from the bore of the barrel to the choke section which is normally then parallel.

In older guns the choked portion of the barrel can be up to 4″ long including the cones whereas in more recent times 2″ is the norm. There are a number of variations in between due to the preferences of different makers and different countries.

Full choke on a 12 bore is 40 thousandths of an inch but this does not necessarily guarantee a full choke pattern will be thrown since the mysteries of choke and pattern quality are not always decided by mere dimensions.

Recessed choke   This becomes necessary when a shooter decides he wants more choke in an 'open' or 'game' bored barrel which presently has, perhaps, 'improved' or 'true cylinder' boring. It can also be required when old long barrels have been, or are to be, shortened, thus removing most if not all of the choke.

Subject to the barrel walls being thick enough a new choke area is bored behind the muzzles. In effect a new cylinder or widened portion of the barrel is created which itself has a new choked portion. However recess choke boring is not always successful when the gun is again tried at the pattern plate. A barrel borer can rarely guarantee a return to more than half choke at best.

Lead-in   The tapered section from the end of the chamber as the diameter reduces to the actual bore of the barrel. The length of taper or 'lead in' varies.

Striking up   A term given by a barrel filer to the longitudinal filing and burnishing and to the final shaping of the exterior of the barrels. This does not refer to the wheel polishing prior to blacking. Hence well-'struck-up' barrels are those which are filed and burnished to a high standard, normally by hand. Good 'striking up' can be seen by holding the barrels up to a light source and looking along the outsides. If the surface has no lumps or evident rings it is well 'struck up'. Cheap guns are simply burnished and polished.

Rivels   When you look down the barrel and see a series of small waves or corrugations these will have been most probably caused by extreme pressure on the tube either from excessively loaded ammunition, a slight obstruction or oil left in the bore. Rivelling usually indicates thin barrel walls but may be removed just as a dent is. It is a skilled operation.

Dents   A dent (or bruise) is where the barrel has literally suffered a blow causing a dent from the outside but pushing the metal inwards to create a lump inside the bore. This inevitably causes a slight but significant restriction in the bore and should be corrected immediately.

Browning   A brown-coloured finish to the exterior of the barrels which is generally applied to Damascus barrels.

Damascus or 'twist' barrels   Damascus used to be made by means of hot forging and twisting alternate strips of steel and iron around a 'mandrel' or rod of roughly bore size. These were then forged and heat-welded together to form the tube. When 'browned', the iron in the amalgam of metal strips rusted quicker than the steel strips thus creating a light and dark brown pattern. The barrels did not receive the hot steam treatment which turns the surface black but were simply waxed to accentuate the patterns. Many different patterns exist of varying quality and beauty. Beware of damascus barrels which are blacked (or blued) to simulate steel barrels. Guns are no longer made in this way but some are still doing good service. Since many damascus-barrelled guns were only proofed for black powder always check that they have been submitted to, and passed, nitro proof. Barrel blacking (or blueing) is still termed 'browning' by the older gun trade worker.

Blacking (blueing)   A rusting process designed to protect steel barrels and to prevent them glittering when in the shooting field. There are literally hundreds of formulae for blueing. The effect created is one of what appears to be black barrels but which have a blueish gleam. Most guns of whatever quality have blued (or blacked) barrels but the depth and quality of finish varies usually according to price. In practice 'browning, blacking' or 'blueing' are used almost indiscriminately in the gun trade to denote barrel finish. Blueing is the term also applied to the chemical finish of ancillary parts such as the trigger guard, top lever, action cover plate, trigger plate etc.

Fore-end iron   The steel centre of the fore-end assembly. This fits onto the barrels over the loop with the front part nearest the action called the knuckle. Its main function is to push the action up into the hook of the front lump and onto the circle at the same time. In simple terms it locks the action and barrels together.

Fore-end push rod   One of several methods employed to attach or remove the fore-end from the barrels which involves a push rod. This is housed in a tube in the fore-end iron. It has a coiled spring and by pressing the external chequered tip of the rod it releases the fore-end iron from the loop. This 'Anson' push rod fore-end is generally associated with Anson and Deeley action boxlocks (the name of the developers of the action) but the same assembly is used on many sidelock guns not of Anson and Deeley design. Naturally there are many other types of fore-end fitting ranging from simple 'snap on' fore-ends, which have no catch and are pulled off and snapped on against a spring, or various other types of catches such as the 'Deeley and Edge' or 'Grip' fore-end.

Kickers   The job of kickers is to strike the rear ends of the ejectors and thus cause them to throw the cartridge clear of the chambers. They protrude from the base of the fore-end iron where it fits into the knuckle of the action. These work independently when one or both barrels are fired. Naturally their position varies according to the type of action encountered, i.e. side-by-side or over-and-under.

Breech ends   These are the two, often ball-shaped, sculpturings of the rear of the action between the top lever and the action faces. Each corresponds to a barrel. These are either plain or have engraved or chiselled designs upon them according to quality and taste. These designs take the form of simple scroll or other engraving but on high-quality guns are often chiselled into patterns displaying oak leaves and claws.

Fences   A gun has 'beaded fences' when a small raised fillet is chiselled and shaped around the rear of the breech ends.

Turnscrew   This is the gunmaker's name for his screwdriver. Its shape differs quite considerably to a normal screwdriver. It normally has a short blade, the point of which has been filed to give a hollow ground shape to fit a screw slot closely. Its broad flat handle assists a maximum grip.

Snap caps   Dummy cartridges which are used to allow the firing pins to be dropped without damage. They are also used to test the firing and ejection mechanism of a gun. The imitation firing cap will be spring loaded to give way as the firing pin strikes them thus buffering the blow as a cartridge will.

Smoke black   The time-honoured use of a small can of paraffin punched with a hole and fitted with a wick, which when lit gives off a yellow flame emitting a thin wisp of black smoke. This is used by gunmakers for slightly sooting the flats of action and barrels of a gun to show, by the appearance of silver 'high spots' when the gun is shut, if there is any flaw in the jointing of action to the barrels.

Blacking down   When the foregoing process is used to achieve the final near-perfect fit between the barrels and the action.

Stock   The stock has two functions – one is to house the action, while the other is to ensure that the gun is positioned against the shoulder to steady it and to take the shock or recoil of firing. Ideally it should be of a length and shape so that the barrels are correctly aligned to the shooter's master eye.

Stocks are available in many different shapes and styles depending on the type of shooting that is required of the gun. The standard game gun will usually have a straight hand stock and this is always best suited to double trigger guns permitting the hand to slide easily back to the rear trigger.

Single trigger guns which do not need the sliding of the hand can be fitted with a half or even full pistol grip stock. In older guns the half pistol stock has a rounded cap whereas the full pistol often has a flat horn cap fitted. Nowadays the two are so much alike that it is often difficult to tell the difference. To some extent it depends on what the maker chooses to call it!

Bend (or drop)   The 'bend' or 'drop' of a stock is measured by continuing a line along the top rib of the barrels and measuring the drop at the comb of the stock and the drop to the heel of the butt. This determines whether or not the top rib will correctly align with the shooter's eye when the gun is mounted.

Generally shooters with long necks will need more drop at comb and heel than those with shorter necks.

Length The length of the stock is measured from the centre of the front trigger to the centre of the heel of the butt. Similar measurements can be taken from the heel and toe of the stock. These measurements and others are part of the ritual of having a gun made to fit your particular needs or even one altered.

Cast A standard stock will normally be made with a bend to the right of between ¼″ and ½″ so that the barrels line up with the master eye. This is called 'cast off' and should fit the average shooter with a right master eye. Guns which are 'cast on' i.e. the stock is bent to the left, are needed by those who are left handed with a left master eye and mount the gun from the left shoulder. In this case the faces or flats of the triggers are normally reversed for comfort as sometimes is the sequence of firing the barrels.

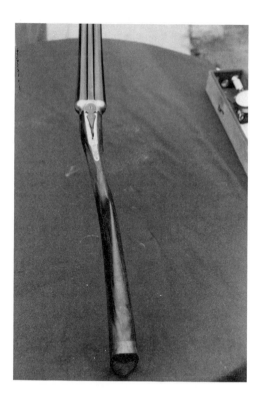

Crossover (or 'crosseyed' stock) This is a stock with a large amount of cast off which enables a right-handed shooter with a left master eye to shoot from the right shoulder. In effect the stock is bent so as to cross the shooter's face. Shooters with a left master eye who are right handed are better advised to learn to shoot from the left shoulder. Alterations will still be necessary and will include 'casting on' or bending the stock to the left, reversing the triggers and their faces so that the pad of the forefinger meets rounded rather than sharp edges, reversing the firing sequence of the barrels and reversing the chokes from right to left.

Try-gun   A gun with a normal action and barrels but with a stock which is adjustable, by means of a spanner or key, to be made different in length, cast, drop or pitch. By shooting, usually at clay targets, the try-gun can be progressively altered to the point where the shooter performs best. Measurements of the try-gun are then carefully taken and used in either building a new gun, fitting a new stock or altering the present stock to match the try-gun's measurements.

Fore-end wood   Most standard English game guns are fitted with a narrow fore-end known as a 'splinter' fore-end. The broader type, which fills the hand and wraps partly around the barrels, is the American 'Beaver Tail' since that is what it resembles. However in English game shooting the hand is extended up the barrels and does not grip the fore-end which is then simply there to cover the fore-end iron.

On many over-and-unders (particularly sporting or 'field' guns) the fore-end is much larger and wraps up over the bottom barrel: in this case the front of the fore-end can be properly gripped. Some over-and-under fore-ends have a pronounced swelling near the tip which acts as a hand stop. This is called a 'tulip' or 'Schnabel' fore-end being also found on many sporting rifles.

Panels   These are the flat areas of wood that are found on either side of the head of the stock where it joins the rear of a boxlock action. Naturally they are not always present, some stocks being rounded, and are never used in sidelock guns since the rear of the lock plate fills where a 'panel' would be.

Drop points   Embellishments that add to the appearance of a gun. Drop points (occasionally called 'dropper points') are the pear drop shapes that appear on a boxlock stock and are an extension to the flat panel where the wood has been sculpted to form what many also refer to as a 'tear drop'. An alternative expression is that a stock has 'points and tear drops'. Drop (or dropper) points also occur on many sidelock stocks but in this case they are simply an extension to the point of the border around the lock plate recess.

Horns   The foremost part of the detached stock (actually side extensions to the interior of the head of the stock). These protrusions are carved to help fit into the metal of the action body to make a better fit and discourage sideways movement.

Shield   At the top and centre of the action's breech a small area of metal has been machined or filed to finish and match the end of the top rib of the barrels where it fits against the action face.

Breech pin   The breech pin is found underneath the closed top lever on conventional side-by-side guns also on some over-and-under guns of English and a few of foreign manufacture. It passes through the stock and screws into the trigger plate clamping the action to the stock. It is also known as the 'body' pin or screw.

Hand   The 'hand' of the stock (frequently called the 'small' of the stock) is the slender part of the stock between the action and the butt stock proper around which the shooter's trigger hand will grasp the gun.

Hand pin   This screws up from underneath passing through the rear end of the trigger plate, through the 'hand' or 'small' of the stock and into the underside of the tang of the action strap.

Stock bolt   This is commonly used in many modern over-and-under as well as automatic, 'pump' action and some boxlock guns. It is a long steel bolt which passes through the stock from the heel and screws into the back of the action, thus securing the action to the stock. It is usually satisfactory but it effectively prevents a gun using it having its stock altered to fit a shooter who may need much 'cast off' or 'cast on'. It normally allows very little stock alteration.

Lock pin   A metal pin (or bolt), used on sidelock guns, which is threaded at one end and which passes through one lock plate, through the wood of the stock to screw into the opposite lock plate, thus pulling both lock plates tight into the wood. On some sidelock guns, this pin has a lever instead of a conventional screw head which permits the screw to be turned with the thumb to detach the locks at any time. It is then said to have 'hand detachable' locks.

Safety slide   These vary slightly in shape depending upon the make of gun and can be found working on the underneath of the top tang or 'strap' on most decent-quality English guns. It also connects to the safety thumbpiece. Foreign boxlocks however usually accommodate the 'safety slide' on the trigger plate which connects to the rear end of the bolt and safety thumbpiece. The safety slide is sometimes responsible for the safety thumbpiece returning to the safe position as the top lever is worked, preparatory to opening the gun.

Articulated trigger   Usually found on the front trigger of some double-triggered guns. The trigger blade has been machined and is in two pieces, allowing the front trigger to pivot forward independently of its blade. The purpose of the articulated front trigger is rather obscure. Perhaps it is intended to prevent the back of the front trigger from striking the finger on the rear trigger or to permit the use of thick gloves when shooting, permitting a gloved finger to fit between the triggers.

Spindle   This sometimes passes through the action under the trigger plate and into the base of the top lever although is more often a tube into which the top lever fits or alternatively part of the top lever itself (occasionally known as the 'barrel').

Bolt   When the top lever is moved to the right, the bolt is the flat slab of metal which moves rearwards out of the 'bites' or slots in the barrel lumps. On closing the barrels the bolt moves forward into the 'bites' and locks and holds the action and barrels together.

Top lever   This is the lever which fits into the top of the action body; when moved to the right it withdraws the bolt (mentioned above) allowing the gun to be opened. In guns with 'automatic' (i.e. self-returning) safety catches, it also returns the safety to safe by actually operating an internal push rod which is in contact with the rear of the bolt. The top lever is the most popular of the several methods of locking the gun shut.

Safety thumbpiece   To be found working in a slot in the rear end of the top tang or strap of the action. Its fairly obvious function is to lock the triggers when positioned rearward i.e. being then on 'safe', thus preventing the triggers from being accidentally pressed. The reader should be warned that this does *not* render the gun safe, since it could still fire if dropped or jarred. An automatic safety catch, referred to above, will operate when the top lever is pressed as the gun is being opened, until pushed forward or 'off' preparatory to firing. A 'non-auto' safe will simply stay in whichever position it was left whether the gun has been opened or not.

Safety catches   Apart from the thumbpiece safety catch positioned behind the top lever on the top tang of a conventional gun, many other types can be encountered. Most of the guns made by W. W. Greener, and based on the 'Empire' action, employ a side safety let into the left side of the stock near the head. This is a 'doll's head' type of safety. On pump action and automatic shotguns the safety is often a simple button catch which passes through the rear of the trigger guard.

In much older guns there have been 'grip safeties' which have a lever fitted parallel to the trigger guard and operate as the gun is gripped in mounting. Another was a safe lever in the heel plate of the gun which came off as the gun was pressed against the shoulder. Other devices have been used over the years.

Trigger plate   Fits into the base of the action on the opposite side and parallel with the top tang or strap. In the case of double triggers two narrow slits are machined into it to accept the trigger blades. Both the 'hand pin' and the 'breech' or body pin are secured by it.

On most English boxlock guns a separate cover plate is fitted to the base of the action which is cut out to fit the front of the trigger plate. On many cheaper boxlock guns the bottom plate and trigger plate are often made as one piece (this economy measure is then known as the base plate).

Trigger guard   Screws into the front of the trigger plate and follows the contour of the stock (fitting into a channel) and looping round to guard the trigger(s). Guards can be found with a rolled edge (sometimes called a 'railed' trigger guard) which takes the feel of an otherwise sharp edge away.

The trigger guard tang (or tail) can be long or short depending upon the shape of the stock or the quality of the gun. A short 'tang' is usually secured by a single wood screw with an engraved head. A long tang normally has two screws securing it to the stock.

Action   A term for both boxlock and sidelock guns being the metal block recessed and shaped to accommodate most of the moving parts.

Action face   When the gun closes the face of the action accepts and fits flush with the flat or face of the barrel ends.

Back action   A type of sidelock gun where the working parts on the sidelock plate and the lock plate itself are fitted into recesses cut from the side of the head of the stock as opposed to being partially fitted into recesses machined in the side of the action bar. In this latter case the gun is technically described as a bar lock. These expressions are equally applied to hammer guns i.e. with external hammers which are normally cocked manually.

Long body action   This is when the 'action bar' or 'body' is longer than normal from the action face to the knuckle on which the barrels rotate open. These longer (and thicker) actions are often used for heavy 'pigeon' guns and wildfowling guns e.g. magnums. One make which employed both short (standard) and long body (heavyweight) actions is the Greener 'Empire' model and its variants.

Striker holes   The hole on each side of the action face through which the firing pins or 'strikers' pass to be able to hit the primers (or caps) in the base of the cartridges and thus fire them.

Disc set strikers   The action face is bored with a hole which is then threaded and a metal plug with a hole through its centre is screwed into the hole. The plug is known as a 'disc' and the separate striker fits inside together with a return spring. In this case the hammers hit the back of the firing pin instead of the hammer noses being pointed i.e. in one piece. This system allows the easy removal and replacement of the strikers without the need also to replace the whole hammer. Strangely, in practice, disc set strikers are frequently more prone to breakage than the solid tumbler/hammer type. This is due to the loose firing pin occasionally sticking in the firing pin hole and failing to withdraw. The point of the pin can then be sheared off as the barrels are shut.

Vent pins   A small threaded pin with a very fine hole drilled through it. The pin is then screwed into the action at the underside of the balls of breech ends. This allows any excessive rearward-moving gases to escape through the vent when the gun is fired. Some old guns have narrow slots machined into a small channel from the firing pin hole across the action face venting at each side of the action. Vent pins are only to be found on guns with disc set strikers.

Action flats   This is the flat part of the action immediately in front of and at right-angles to the action face to which the barrel flats fit. Proof marks will be found on the bridge between the two slots or on one or both flats.

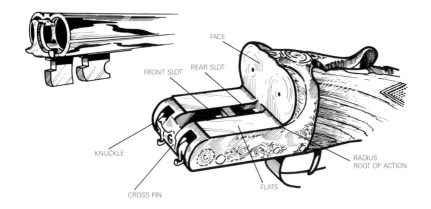

Root   The radiused area in the corner between the action flats and the face. This radius reduces the otherwise serious risk of the action cracking at that point, particularly during proof firing. Naturally there is a corresponding radius on the lower edge of the barrel flats to which the root radius mates.

Toes   The front part of the action flats.

Knuckle   The rounded part of the action immediately in front of the toes.

Top strap (or tang)   The strip of metal protruding from and extending behind the top of the action. It is tapered in thickness and houses the top lever and safety catch.

Breech pin   Secures the action to the stock. It passes through the top tang and screws into a pillar on the trigger plate. It is the thickest screw used and is the central feature which holds the action and stock together.

Hand pin   This connects the rear of the trigger plate and the top tang (or strap) together. It passes through the rear of the trigger plate and screws into the underside of the tang.

Furniture   The furniture is all the smaller, exterior metal parts of the gun and includes the trigger plate, cover plate (or base plate), triggers and trigger guard, top lever, safety catch etc. Normally the 'furniture' parts are all chemically blued before assembly onto the gun.

Trigger pulls   The amount of pressure required to release the sear from the bent of the hammer and thereby fire the gun. It is measured in pounds and is tested by a small spring scale with a graduated barrel (rather like a spring balance or weighing scales). The average weight of pulls for a normal gun are

3 to 3¹/₂ lb on the front trigger, 4 to 4¹/₂ lb for the rear trigger.

Recoil   This is the rearward force which is exerted on the gun as a cartridge is fired. In effect the gun is thrown backward against the stock which itself flexes whilst the remaining recoil is absorbed by the shooter's shoulder. In practical terms most shooters are not overconscious of recoil since its action is too rapid to be detected and transmitted by the brain as discomfort before recoil is complete. This is particularly the case if the shooter's attention is concentrated on the target or result of the shot.

Recoil can be uncomfortable due to excessive head space (see that paragraph) or if the cartridge is too strong for the gun's weight e.g. using a 'heavy load' cartridge in a light game gun. Recoil can also be most noticeable if the stock is a poor fit for the particular shooter. The only remedy to this is to have the stock altered or obtain a new stock or a new better fitting gun. A stock may be lengthened by adding a recoil pad, a thicker heel plate (using ebonite) or a piece of wood of the same grain as the stock. This latter method is rarely completely unnoticeable since matching grains perfectly is extremely difficult.

Recoil pad   A rubber compound pad fitted to the butt end of the stock and designed to absorb some of the recoil as the gun is fired. The material used is of critical importance since a pad which is too soft will not absorb much of the shock and a pad which is too hard will not have time appreciably to reduce the recoil which reaches the shoulder.

Drag   Something that should not be present in the feel of good trigger pulls, and is also described as 'creep'. It describes the feeling of stretching experienced if the triggers meet a lot of friction resistance from the sears and also denotes a poor fit or lack of proper polishing to the sear and/or bent. It can also be caused by the arm of the sear bending.

Sear   An internal part of the mechanism which has two features i.e. it has a nose and an arm. This part is angled or 'L' shaped and the nose fits into a 'bent' or vee slot and is, over a number of years, subjected to much wear. Unless correctly made and heat treated it will become rounded. This can seriously affect the poundage (weight) and crispness of the trigger pull. Pulls can suddenly become dangerously light or excessively heavy and 'dragging'.

Single triggers   This allows the firing of each barrel without the need to move the trigger finger. Broadly speaking these are made as one of two types i.e. 'selective' where the shooter can choose whether to fire the open or more choked barrel first. Selection is usually made by means of an additional two positions of the safety catch or some other switch device. Often the single trigger is left to fire conventionally i.e. the open barrel first and the choked barrel second. The shooter can then choose to reverse the sequence only when required.

'Non-selective' single triggers compel the firing of the open barrel first and the choked barrel second. The benefits obtained are that a shooter used to a single barrel or repeater gun can readily adapt to a single trigger double gun and one can shoot in gloved hands.

The disadvantages are that all single-trigger systems are more prone to mechanical failure than double triggers. This can take the form, depending on type, of failing to fire the second barrel at all or a double discharge where both barrels fire virtually simultaneously. Both events can be very disconcerting.

The predictable reality is that good-quality single-trigger guns give less trouble, in the main, than cheaper guns. Many cheap guns with single-triggers employ poor materials, and in guns, as elsewhere, you receive exactly what you pay for!

Intercepting sear   This is a safety device incorporated in the lever work of many sidelock and some high-quality boxlock guns. The intercepting sears are usually fitted alongside the conventional sears and if the main sear is accidentally jarred out of bent through the gun being dropped or knocked over, or the opposing barrel being fired, the intercepting sear continues to retain the hammer. This facility operates whether the safety catch is on or off. However, it should be clearly understood that the intercepting sear will *not* work if the triggers are pressed inadvertently, or intentionally, with the safe off. It is extremely unwise to expect the intercepting sear to be a substitute for safe gun handling.

Since the intercepting sear is normally a feature of high-quality guns, which are usually very well made, the need for this feature is diminished. On guns of poorer quality which rarely have intercepting sears the need for them is much greater. In summary, the intercepting sear is usually present where it is least needed and absent where it is most necessary.

Hammer or tumbler   A shaped block of metal which is driven forward, propelled by the main spring, and hits the back of the striker or itself has a point which passes through the striker hole to fire the cartridge. It is released by pressure on the trigger freeing the sear. A 'bent' is cut into the hammer to take the sear nose (a 'bent' is a small 'vee' slot – its correct shape is most important). The hammer must also be correctly heat treated to enable it to stand up to hitting the striker or cartridge many hundreds, perhaps thousands, of times in its life.

When the trigger is pulled it lifts the nose of the sear out of the bent of the hammer thus allowing the hammer to travel forward and strike the cap in the cartridge or hit the separate striker. Hammer, sear and main spring are housed on the inside wall of the lock plates of a sidelock gun.

Cocking dogs   These protrude from each side of the action and through the knuckle and, when the gun opens, they pivot, so recocking the hammers.

Cocking indicators   Though now a rarity, various devices have been tried to enable the shooter to see when a hammerless gun is cocked. These range from small pins which protrude through the sides of the action which stick out when the gun is cocked and lie flush when the hammers are down. 'Crystal Indicators' were literally small clear perspex windows in the side of the action body through which one peered to see whether or not the hammers were back or down. On some sidelocks there is a gold-lined slot which is in the end of the tumbler pivot pin. This points backwards when the gun is cocked, forwards when the hammer is down. Whichever type is encountered the gun should be regarded as cocked and dangerous at all times!

Overdraft   When the gun has been 'broken' i.e. opened to its fullest extent 'overdraft' is the amount of clearance between the top of the face of the action and the chambers. If there is insufficient overdraft the gun will be awkward to load since there is hardly enough space to slide in fresh cartridges. Overdraft is sometimes described as 'gape' i.e. the amount the gun opens. Conversely, should there be too much overdraft, the gun will be harder to close easily due to the wider angle of opening.

Boxlock   So called because its shape is box like. In general terms less cost is involved in its manufacture when compared to a sidelock because the action houses most of its mechanism within the body. There are also fewer parts than in a sidelock gun.

    Due to being machined to accommodate the mechanism the boxlock is thought to be the weaker of the two models – though in practical terms this is seldom the case since most, if not all, guns are designed to be quite strong enough for normal service.

Sidelock   Usually more costly to manufacture than an equivalent-quality boxlock. A greater amount of time and skill is required in making and fitting the sidelocks and the overall finish. The other features of a sidelock gun normally receive more attention too.

Lapping   A gun trade term used to describe the process of polishing the bore of a shotgun tube either to burnish after boring or remove slight pitting. It entails the use of a long rod and a lathe or rotating machine.

Over & under   This is a gun where one barrel is fitted on top of the other, which finds favour with most clay shooters and those who say they prefer a single sight plane. They are available in both boxlock and sidelock models and of course ejectors and non-ejectors. English handmade over-and-unders are among the most expensive over-and-unders in the world since very few were made compared to the large number of side-by-sides. The over-and-under was never popular in Great Britain until relatively recent times and some British over-and-unders were not well designed.

Main spring   The largest spring in the gun. In most English guns it is of flat section and forged into a vee shape and so called a 'vee' spring and which connects directly to the hammer. In many modern guns, particularly over-and-unders, the vee spring has, due to the gun's design, been superseded by coil springs.

Side clips   These are projections which extend out and forwards from each side of the action face which are broadly a part of the breech ends. They mate with a bevel filed on the outside of the barrel ends. Their purpose is to strengthen the breech closure by preventing any sideways or lateral movement of the barrels when the gun is closed.

Side plates   Flat pieces of metal shaped and added to the rear of a boxlock action by being inlet into the stock and designed to resemble a sidelock lock plate. These are purely a form of decoration and can be seen on over-and-unders and side-by-side guns. The plates often have the engraving running over the join strengthening the illusion that the gun is in fact a sidelock. While they have no practical function they enhance the appearance of a gun.